# A QUESTION OF HEALING

# A Question of Healing

*The Reflections of a Doctor and Priest*

Gareth Tuckwell and David Flagg

Foreword by Lord Coggan

**Fount**
*An Imprint of* HarperCollins*Publishers*

Fount Paperbacks is an imprint of
HarperCollins*Religious*
Part of HarperCollins*Publishers*
77-85 Fulham Palace Road, London W6 8JB

First published in Great Britain
in 1995 by Fount Paperbacks

1 3 5 7 9 10 8 6 4 2

A catalogue record for this book is
available from the British Library

0 00 627921-0

Printed and bound in Great Britain by
HarperCollins Manufacturing Glasgow

# Acknowledgements

We acknowledge that there are many written sources from which we have consciously or subconsciously drawn, but not always made reference to, and we are grateful for these.

More specifically we wish to thank the following:

**The Burrswood Care Team** – we could not have learnt without their challenge and confrontation; we could not have kept going without their support and without encouragement from the whole community.

**The Trustees of the Dorothy Kerin Trust** – for recognizing the importance of speaking and writing as key tasks within the work at Burrswood.

**The Rev. Anne Long** – for having a heart for our partnership and for oiling its wheels at regular intervals.

**Edward England** – for encouragement to keep on writing and for releasing copyright from *Healing and Wholeness* magazine to us.

**Veronica Ross** – for 'blood, sweat and tears' over Words for Windows and for working to endless deadlines.

**Ruth and Mary**, our wives – for long-suffering and living with the displaced emotions that accompany us at the end of the day.

# Contents

# Foreword

I am very glad that this book has been written. It is the result of the close co-operation, within a wider team and over a period of years, between a doctor and a priest. The strength of the book lies in its combination of medical skill and spiritual insight.

If the reader is looking for an easy answer – a kind of panacea for the ills that flesh is heir to – he will not find it here. But if he is looking for a frank approach to problems such as cancer or ME or bulimia, and moreover for writing which does not use technical terms without explaining them, he will find much to meet his needs or direct him to where further help can be found.

Both writers are men of deep Christian conviction. Their faith is a very earthy one – no wonder, for they write of One who 'became flesh and made his home among us'. But their faith looks up to heaven and to a God who longs that all his creatures should share his wholeness.

May this book enter many a home and many a hospital ward.

*Donald Coggan*
*Winchester*

# Introduction

## CHRISTOPHER

This book was, in one sense, born out of a death. The human link through whom we were introduced was Christopher. He was Gareth and Mary's nephew and had suffered brain damage at birth. Christopher lived in David's parish where he and his wife Ruth were closely involved in giving support to Christopher and his parents. At twenty-one months Christopher died, having taught us all much about the mystery of healing and suffering. This was then the context in which we first met and spoke together, not least in the garden of Christopher's home after his funeral. This coincided with the point at which Gareth was being interviewed for the directorship of Burrswood and David was contemplating a move into chaplaincy work of some kind. What was, and still seems, significant was the name of Christopher – literally 'bearer of Christ'. David spoke about this at the funeral; how there were important things that Christopher achieved for Christ and His Kingdom despite his severe disability and short life span – things which the rest of us in our so-called wellbeing could not have achieved in three score years and ten. Christopher was the unique 'bearer of Christ' who, because he introduced us to each other, has a special place in our relationship, and not surprisingly we see the theme of his life – Christ being found in the midst of the agony – unravelling more in our work at Burrswood and in the writing of this book.

## BURRSWOOD

In our subsequent work together in the Burrswood setting we

attempted to build a doctor/priest partnership which was more than a token or symbolic relationship. Dorothy Kerin at Burrswood had always related to the medical profession and seen the importance of involving doctors at the highest level of the work which she undertook. In developing further the complementary roles of medicine and spirituality in order to create a piece of closely coordinated and interdisciplinary teamwork in the Burrswood Medical Centre, we dared to believe that we responded to the vision of Dorothy Kerin as appropriate to a new generation. Hopefully we were gently pioneering something in the Burrswood care team which speaks to the medical and spiritual worlds alike.

Burrswood, for all its peace and beauty for those who stay there, is not some ivory tower of quiet contemplation from which this book was written. No, the anvil on which this writing was forged was the daily rhythm spanning some years of the in-depth care provided by a remarkable house, a place which has come to change us as much as we changed it. At first it was hard really to appreciate the value of a residential setting for this ministry. There seemed the danger of such a place being viewed as a shrine rather than a safe setting for a personal journey into health and healing. We gradually had our eyes opened to the amazing things that God is able to do when those who are sick in body, mind and spirit are enabled to let go. Letting go into skilled hands within a beautiful and safe environment often allows a deep encounter with the God who heals. Space to be alone, an objective approach from carers whose insight is not swayed by past events and, above all, a tidal wave of love from a caring and nurturing Christian community are transforming. In one sense Burrswood is like a giant rubbish dump! We have been amongst a team of dustmen helping to off-load the rubbish at the foot of the Cross – because only Jesus can take it and redeem it in his love.

This process was not a simple one because as we faced the pain and brokenness of others, so we had to face our own. There was often no opportunity to stand still before God and to off-load before him but the significance of the daily Eucharist within the community was perhaps greater than met the eye. Those able to partake would leave the burdens of their own and others' making at the foot of the Cross, 'holding all silently up to him' (Dorothy Kerin). Frank Lake described a daily Eucharist during a residential conference as feeding upon 'the realities which enable me and others to go boldly through the day into the most mind-shattering corners of our human catastrophe'. The other rituals of the day were also significant. Team meetings were a crucial coming together, whether they were enjoyable or stressful. Somehow mutual support enabled a debriefing, a check on one another's health in the here and now. Other support structures were vital.

## VIEWING THE WHOLE

Not surprisingly there are recurrent themes in this book. The emphasis on an interweaving of medical and spiritual approaches to care is inevitable because it has been part of our mission together. We all carry pain and 'dis-ease' in some areas of our lives but because inner pain is less acceptable and costlier to share, it is more often the physical pain and disease that is readily encountered and demands attention. Yet, on listening, we may find that the root of real distress and pain is not in physical illness but rather is held within the emotional, psychological, social or spiritual experience of the individual. This theme is more fully explored in the chapter on inner healing.

## TEAMWORK

Inevitably we have a heart-longing for interdisciplinary working within the wider community which also emerges in these pages. The insights of both pastor and doctor need to be harnessed for the delivery of the most appropriate treatment and care. Teamwork is something in which we have had to invest heavily. The overlapping roles of the team members, representing a number of disciplines, seem especially important to us for what they encompass: an area of creativity, a shared purpose in Christ that belongs to the group. This area of creativity can only exist when each member accepts that their professional position may be modified. The encountering of suffering calls for this kind of partnership where each member has an equal voice and is willing to show flexibility and adaptability. Perhaps this book is a symbol of that partnership and our relationship.

As Dr Murray Parkes observed, ' . . . care is a matter of human relationships. There are skills to be learned and insights which can be gained from reading books, but the challenge and the reward of care arises from the fact that it demands that we use the whole of ourselves to relate to our fellow human beings who are in trouble. This can only be learned by experience in a community in which relationships are valued and fostered.' We would echo this and quickly discovered that in close teamwork there is something very uncomfortable as different personalities, temperaments and disciplines come up against each other. But in that close working there is also a merging which is life-giving. It is part of the way in which Christ works through us all together as we struggle to move in step with him. Some of that merging is reflected in our own ability to write 'as one' – not easy but possible when the thinking becomes the same at crucial points.

## THE CHURCH AND HEALING

Much of what we write springs from a concern for what passes for the promotion of 'healing' in our churches, and issues related to this recur in the following pages. We recognize that often the professional world of medicine and other caring disciplines fail to respect what the Church offers – perhaps for good reason. The healing movement itself becomes sick when bad pastoral practice is cloaked in spiritual phraseology; when the 'strong' insist that the 'weak' believe for a cure; when 'deliverance' is seen as the only resort if the helper is stuck; when carers, driven by their own needs, always need to solve everything. There is potentially a frightening level of abuse – not least in the area of terminally ill people being pressurized to think in terms of total recovery. Sometimes the healing movement looks ominously like a collusion between the would-be healers and the people who can thrive only on their ministrations! So a common theme for us is that the 'sick' have much to teach the 'well', and not least within the Church's own walls.

## INTEGRATING CHURCH TRADITIONS

At the time of writing, the issues within the Christian healing movement are still dominated by the concerns of the charismatic renewal and its subsequent 'waves'. Both of us would want to assert positively our own indebtedness to the renewal movement. But writing as we do from the context of a centre which was founded within the Anglo-Catholic and sacramental tradition, we constantly draw attention to emphases far broader than the repetition of charismatic jargon. As with our emphasis on teamwork we would hope that the Church itself can 'get it together' in terms of drawing upon the strengths of all traditions. It is our experience that, for example, the gentle and predictable ministry of Burrswood, with the life of the Spirit tending to be expressed within a sacramental and liturgical framework, creates a powerful healing ethos for those who come in great suffering. The giving of space in every sense, space in which symbolism can be used by God rather than heavily imposed by the helper, gives a real 'elbow room' to the Spirit which more intense and dramatic approaches may fail to facilitate. Again the spaces which only silence and aloneness provide are so vital for healing to happen.

## SUFFERING

A major thread in all that we write here is the whole way we come at the issue of suffering. We point the reader in particular to our final chapter. Christians with a strong emphasis on healing often display a correspondingly weak understanding of suffering. It may be implied, or even explicitly stated, that suffering for the name of Christ is the only suffering Christians are meant to experience. All other suffering, so a rather simple 'substitution' theory goes, was borne by Christ alone on the cross so that we need not bear it. It is not hard to see how this view implicitly but directly affects the whole way we may deal with others in their suffering. We can only begin to offer them real hope if with them we struggle to find a meaning within the suffering which takes us well beyond the simple view. What we are doing is developing some kind of theology of suffering: finding God within it rather than only without it. In offering this, we acknowledge the influence of Frank Lake who pointed to the grace needed to stay with pain in the strength of the Lord who went through it and not round it.

## LOSS

A key area of suffering is that of loss which is another recurring theme in our writing. It was perhaps the major common factor in our work with those who came to stay at Burrswood: loss not only in the death of loved ones but in all the experiences of life's phases. It was often true that people were helped simply by the recognition of another that their losses were real and by the shared naming of their grief. There is no simple way round the bearing of griefs and sorrows. Easing the way through involves some understanding of the path of grief *and* a confidence in the Lord whose risen life proclaims that every Good Friday gives way to a new Easter Day.

6

# WRITING TOGETHER

In the early days of our partnership we wrote individually for the *Burrswood Herald*. Edward England, then publisher of *Renewal* magazine, felt that the *Herald* deserved a wider readership. With characteristic generosity and vision he launched the magazine *Healing and Wholeness* at the start of 1991. He invited us to write together on a regular basis for the new magazine which rapidly achieved a circulation of close to ten thousand quarterly.

Despite living in Community, working and relaxing together, writing together was a real challenge. With each question that was to be the basis of an article we would meet to talk around the subject, decide the key areas to be covered and divide the work. Some paragraphs are recognizably by one or the other of us, but we aim to 'own' it all. Some are one sentence by one and the next by the other! In the course of our working, writing, and sometimes speaking together, we developed a way of thinking about what healing really means which we particularly develop in the final chapter. The book was written over a period of time and, as we have said, not by withdrawing from activity in order to reflect and express ourselves.

# HEALTH FOR THE FUTURE

We hope this book will also provide some pointers in the way provision is made for the health of our society. In these days of purchasers and providers, of protocols and outcomes, it is all too easy to have a superficial focus and to conclude that any particular 'outcome' is the most satisfactory when the individual is physically independent of professional care in the shortest possible time and at the lowest possible cost. Yet, as we have emphasized in this book, good 'outcomes' are so much more than this and cannot be quantified solely in terms of physical health. The future wellbeing of each one of us is dependent on every level of pain being recognized and addressed in a personal and individual way. Health is not administered one to the other but experienced in concert with others. It is inevitable that our own pain surfaces whilst listening to the suffering of so many in need and it can be a challenge to distinguish their true cry from ours. We recognize that we are all sick – there is no 'us' and 'them'.

# THE JOURNEY GOES ON

We, together and individually, continue to change and to grow in the way we now understand and express the truths we were struggling with in these chapters. Because of this, it is by no means a carefully worked-out thesis. We have attempted to answer the questions posed from a medical perspective along with faith and biblical insight. We have left the chapters in the order in which they were written to help the reader to pick up something of our own journey. Prior to the publication of this book we reviewed our writing, some of which originated up to four years before. It is inevitable that there are a few statements that we would now change, yet to do this would seem to say that this process of gaining new insights into the mystery of health and healing will not go on. We are all hopefully on a journey of understanding that will continue for the rest of our lives. We have come to appreciate the wisdom of David Jenkins when he wrote: 'Health is a value and a vision word which has both to be brought constantly down to earth and to be related persistently to a promise, an aim and a hope which lies ahead and above us.'

# *1* Praying for a Friend with Cancer

**Q** A friend of mine has been diagnosed as having inoperable cancer. How should I pray for her? Should I expect God to heal her miraculously?

**A** Your question raises a number of issues and we want to answer under three headings:

## WAYS OF PRAYING FOR YOUR FRIEND

### *Listening to God*
'The Lord . . . wakens my ear to listen' (Isaiah 50:4).

Your first prayer might be, '*How* should I pray Lord?' and 'What is in your heart and mind for my friend?

Why not meet *with others* to listen to God? When you are together God's word can be checked out and there is less chance of wishful thinking. In a group you will also find support and encouragement to go on praying.

There is probably someone else you could ask to listen to God on behalf of your friend. Often those outside a situation are more able to listen in a detached way to what is in God's heart and mind. There may also be communities or centres in your area which offer a ministry of intercession (check that it is confidential before you give too much detail).

You may feel you are hearing nothing from the Lord. This doesn't mean 'stop praying'. Rather, God allows you to live with uncertainty because that is really the nature of faith. He wants you to trust him with your friend even though he has not revealed a way through. He wants you to go on praying in the Spirit.

It may be that you receive a word of knowledge giving insight into the situation, or a prophecy revealing something of God's purposes. These can direct your prayers and praises more specifically. But beware. Words from God should not be used as 'proof' that 'everything will be all right'; just as words from the doctor should not be used to prove that everything will go 'wrong'. Keep a sense of balance and perspective. Be careful of sharing specific 'promises' with your friend. A true word from the Lord is characterized by a sense of 'aha!' – that is, it includes an element of surprise with an element of recognition. It is never simply a comfortable confirmation of what you wanted to hear.

As you listen to God you may also become aware of action you should take for your friend – e.g. should you get involved and visit her, or simply pray at a distance? Through this situation of pain the Lord is also dealing with you, so be ready to hear something for yourself!

### Soaking prayer
'Lord, the one you love is sick' (John 11:3).

In soaking prayer simply hold your sick friend into the love of Jesus. This is usually a prayer of silence and works well in a group. The emphasis is on the love and grace of Jesus soaking into the one who is held into him. You can pray for a relatively long time in this way, either with your friend if she is happy or in a separate place.

### Gut prayer
Paul yearned for his friends with the 'bowels of Jesus Christ' (Philippians 1:8).

The prayer of empathy means putting yourself into your friend's shoes. Again it is often a prayer of silence, or of sighing or groaning (Romans 8:26). Weeping has a real place in intercession. Give God your feelings, which are precious to him, as you identify with your friend's needs. It may also be right to weep with her. We have witnessed beautiful healing moments when tears have been shared with someone who was dying.

### 'On the altar' prayer

'Into your hands I commit . . .' (Psalm 31:5).

In this prayer you let go of your friend and, giving thanks that she has been given to you, you now give her back to God. It is time to take your 'hands off'. You can tell the Lord what you feel he ought to do, but you cannot twist his arm! Putting her on the altar of his love means you abandon her to his perfect will. This may mean that (like Abraham with Isaac, Hebrews 11:19) you 'receive her back as from the dead'. Either way you let go.

### Prayers of affirmation and authority

'Be strong in the Lord' (Ephesians 6:10).

Your authority rests in the lordship of Jesus Christ, and springs from a place of trust, rest and peace. Cultivate this in your praying. Give thanks that God covers your friend with his armour (Ephesians 6:10-18) and gives her complete salvation in Christ. Claim his freedom from all powers of evil.

Some people feel it appropriate to curse a cancer in the name of Jesus or to bind a spirit of infirmity. Don't move into this area with her unless you really have her express permission. Someone experienced in praying for the sick should be with you in this.

## EXPECTING GOD TO HEAL HER

Yes indeed: expect God to *heal her!* This is his promise and as you pray we expect you to witness it. But we have to say this does not necessarily include her being 'miraculously cured'. Nevertheless you can expect some healing of:

## Body

Francis Macnutt in *The Power to Heal* talks about various levels of physical healing, e.g.,

- cessation of pain
- removal of the side effects of treatment, drugs, etc.
- some stabilization of the illness

You can pray confidently for God to bless, often through medical and nursing attention, so that your friend is in a place of relative well-being within the limitations of her illness.

Often the impression is given that physical healing is all or nothing, and this is not usually the case.

## Mind and spirit

Healing for your friend involves her relationship with God and with the people around her, as well as an attitude of mind. Gareth remembers that when his father was dying he commented, 'You know, all those prayers for my healing were answered. The depression I was going into a year ago has left me completely, and so has all the fear of dying: I know it won't be long now.' Healing of mind and spirit is as much a miracle as healing of the body. Moltmann defined true health as 'the strength to live, the strength to suffer, and the strength to die'.

# BEING ALONGSIDE YOUR FRIEND

## Her Agenda

Try not to load her up with yours! Sometimes Christians say and do terrible things to the sick and dying. Listen to where *she* is, and move along with her. Illness and growing weakness take a person through various stages of loss and adjustment, e.g.,

- coming to terms with the diagnosis, which may include denial and avoidance;

- feelings of disgust, loathing and anger towards or about the cancer and its unpleasant manifestations;
- the threatened end of a fulfilling career;
- loss of role — in society, church and family;
- possible loss of parts of the body through surgery, and loss of faculties as the illness progresses;
- frustration, anger, depression as adjustment takes place;
- anxiety about leaving loved ones behind, and anger that they might manage alone;
- fears for the future, e.g., the progressive stages of the illness and what it will be like;
- a desire to heal the past and resolve difficult relationships;
- an enjoyment of life as a 'gift' and of 'in depth' quality time.

So, take your cue from her and stay 'with' her as much as you are able. Often a sick person is more in touch with where things are 'at' than the people around them. So, listen — and pray appropriately.

### Your agenda
You will need support for yourself if you are going to see the situation through. Again, many seriously ill people get dumped by Christian 'friends' because it is hard to stay with suffering. Find a sympathetic listener, possibly someone with listening and counselling skills, who can help you to identify what is going on for you. In this way you will be open to receive what God has for you in the situation, and you will be freed from putting your needs 'onto' your sick friend.

All in all it is at once a precious and a painful situation for you both, and there will be much turmoil and many tears. In whatever way God chooses to heal, heal he will, because healing is his speciality. But be open to that as a process of growth; growth for your friend as she lives with serious illness, and growth for you as you support her.

The true meaning of miracle is 'something to wonder at' and in that context, who knows, there may be many miracles along the way.

## 2 Pills or Prayer?

**Q** I was diagnosed as being manic-depressive eight years ago. Since then I have been taking a drug called lithium which has to be carefully monitored because it can harm the kidneys and thyroid gland. As I have recently had hands laid on me in the name of Jesus for complete healing, should I discontinue lithium?

**A** Your question raises the twin issues of the role of the doctor in our society, and of the relation between spiritual and medical ministrations. Working together as we do we are able to hold together a medical approach with a spiritual one. We recognize that this is not always so easy for the man or woman 'in the street'.

It is right to be wary of blind faith in what the doctor prescribes. 2 Chronicles 16:12 is an intriguing reference to King Asa who did not seek help from the Lord but only from physicians. Mark seems to suggest that spending money on medical treatment may be a wasteful investment (Mark 5:26) while Luke, the physician, would seem judiciously to leave out the comment that the woman in question had consulted doctor after doctor and only got worse.

We have to be aware of modern scientific medicine becoming a religion of its own, with the doctor 'playing God', but it is just as unbalanced for Christians to deny the place of medical understanding and treatment. Medicine rightly practised is one of the gifts of God.

### CONSIDERING DEPRESSION

It may be helpful to look at the whole question of *depression*.

## Medically

Depression as *illness* reflects some of the 'disease' from which human beings suffer. Christians need not feel guilty at being depressed. Seeing depression as illness can alter our reaction to the need for medication. You would probably not throw away your antibiotics, prescribed by the doctor, because you felt guilty about taking them for pneumonia. If there is a drug that might save our life most of us are more than willing to try the benefits of the latest medical technology. You could see your treatment for depression in the same light: it keeps you responding relatively normally to daily life and relationships. Conversely, to stop medication may bring dangers: a number of people with diabetes have died through stopping insulin after prayer for healing.

In medical terms depressive illness can be divided into:

### Reactive or neurotic depression

Triggered by events, e.g. trauma, long-standing 'pain' (physical, psychological, spiritual or relational). It may be a response to loss, hurt, anger, guilt – your hidden or not so hidden agenda.

Triggered by hormonal changes, or physical illness such as glandular fever, meningitis, head injury, major surgery, stroke.

### Endogenous ('arising from within') or psychotic depression

This is often the result of a fragile chemical balance of the neuro-transmitters in the brain, a tendency that can be inherited.

Lithium carbonate, a naturally occurring salt, is especially used in manic-depressive psychosis. It stabilizes the mood and prevents the chemical changes that cause the swing in mood. *Note* that lithium acts slowly and therefore stopping it may not produce an immediate lowering of mood.

## Spiritually

*Oppression* may give rise to depression. The picture is of an objective heavy weight coming down on us. The oppression is like an assault of evil that needs counteracting through prayer in the name and in the power of the blood of Jesus. It may be right for every depressed Christian to be prayed over for this kind of deliverance, in order to deal with any oppression of evil which may be *a* factor in the situation. But just as it is wrong to diagnose clinical depression when the issue is really spiritual oppression, so it is also wrong to insist on viewing all depression in terms of spiritual warfare.

*Underlying factors*, e.g. lifestyle, unhealed hurts, unresolved conflict, repressed anger, unconfessed sin. Any of these and other factors can give rise to depression. All illness is 'saying' something to us. So depression is a means by which our body and mind say 'Hey! – wait a minute. Just take a look at . . .'

As we do take a look at underlying needs, we can then take action in terms of adapting our life style, seeking healing for our hurt, resolving conflict, releasing anger and confessing sin. Often the Lord wants to give us *insight* into our needs before the healing process can begin. We say more about the benefits of counselling and prayer below. We have to be realistic and say that sometimes even after much counselling and prayer ministry, depression may remain or recur. Like other illnesses it can be long-term and part of the great mystery of suffering.

## CASE HISTORIES

Here are two real-life stories which you may find relate to your situation:

A woman with myxoedema (from an underactive thyroid gland) had been well for years on thyroxine tablets. After attending a church healing service she stopped her treatment. In a few months she developed a severe psychotic illness caused by thyroxine deficiency and was admitted to hospital. When her treatment was restored she made a steady recovery.

A man in his thirties had been well on lithium for three years, but he had always felt the disapproval of his Christian friends in relation to his mental illness. He went to a healing service in a church he was visiting, where the minister did not know him.

He later stopped his treatment on the advice of the minister, who did know that this man was having to cope with an enormous loss in his life – that of his daughter leaving home to get married. He became very depressed and psychotic and was admitted to a psychiatric hospital. When he returned to his own church he was made to feel unspiritual, and that his illness was something self-indulgent (sinful) which he should 'snap out of'. He eventually left the church.

## A WAY AHEAD

We would advise you along the following lines:

- See lithium for you as a gift from God. Give thanks over it as you may do over your food and drink and pray that the Lord will bless it to you and remove harmful side effects.
- Understand how and why it works, as we have described above. For example, be aware that it is slow acting so its benefits would be slow to disappear if you did stop it.
- Talk to your doctor about how long term a treatment it is. When he/she sees you keeping well over many months he/she may want to help you reduce it. You should only do this under his/her supervision.
- Taking lithium will emphatically *NOT* stop God wanting to bring you out of depression. We cannot stress this too much. It is not a question of 'faith' *or* 'pills'.
- Encourage your minister and your doctor to work together for your wellbeing. When we are sick there should be two phone calls – one to the elders of the church (James 5) and one to the doctor. Hopefully there is a group of friends from your church who pray regularly for you. You may also want to seek help from a recommended counsellor who is also a Christian. This is in

order to address underlying causes for your depression (it is likely that there are underlying issues in *endogenous* as well as *reactive* depression).

It is not always the right moment for counselling, so be guided by those who are experienced here. Sometimes when we are feeling fragile it is wiser to ask the Lord to 'contain' things and to pray generally for 'healing of the mind'. We need to be in a place of relative strength from which to face our inner pain. He does not 'break the bruised reed'! (Isaiah 42:3).

• Can we gently challenge you with the idea that throwing the lithium down the lavatory might be an attempt to twist God's arm! Look at your motives and beware of stopping treatment through presumption or misunderstanding, or because you cannot accept that some people need to take medication. Stopping the tablets may be an immature response. Cloaking it in spiritual language (as an act of 'faith') does not redeem it. Taking the tablets is, as often as not, the *responsible* path of true caring for yourself. To stop taking them, conversely, is to fail to assume responsibility for your treatment.

## DEPRESSION IN PERSPECTIVE

We want to conclude by encouraging you that you are not alone. The human spirit is vulnerable to depression and some of us are more vulnerable than others. Because Christians are often exposed to great tensions they can be *more* prone to suffering in this way.

Depression is an experience common to the people of God — for example the prophets, especially Jeremiah (20:14). A large number of Christian leaders have suffered with some form of depression, from Martin Luther to David Watson. There are also some 'positive advantages' to suffering in this way. Those of us who are or have been vulnerable to depression and anxiety are, compared to people who do not suffer in this way:

- more likely to seek out places in ourselves which need deep healing – memories, hurts, neurotic patterns, sinful reactions;
- more likely to know ourselves and hopefully accept ourselves as imperfect, inadequate, and dependent upon the grace of God (2 Corinthians 12:9);
- more likely to relate sensitively to others suffering from emotional, psychological, and spiritual distress.

You may not feel the path God has given you to tread is the one you would choose. But do not be pressured by others or by things inside yourself to go for short cuts. Withdrawing your medication is undoubtedly a short cut. God wants even more for you than you want for yourself, and wants to use you to bless others because of what you, even now, are going through.

# *3* Confused about ME?

**Q** I have suffered from exhaustion for two years and my doctor has recently sent me for an ME test which he says is positive. He never really has time to talk to me. I am confused about what ME is and I find myself slipping into being centred on my illness. My ME is in danger of becoming my identity. Can you help?

**A** ME stands for myalgic encephalomyelitis. It is one of the conditions that are collectively known as 'chronic fatigue syndromes'. It presents itself as a group of symptoms that are commonly triggered by a viral infection. These include muscle fatigue and pain, headaches, nausea, aching glands, exhaustion, poor concentration and a number of poorly defined complaints.

Professionals and the public need to accept the existence of this disease which results in a major health problem for many people although the course and severity varies greatly. Sadly some sufferers remain severely disabled and make little progress with mobility despite good motivation.

## THE TESTS FOR ME

Much of the research has been unsatisfactory, partly because there is no standardized laboratory test. Groups of ME sufferers have been studied carefully but the criteria used for defining ME have differed, leading to results that cannot be directly compared. Some research suggests that there is an abnormal immune response to certain enteroviruses that most of us encounter at some stage: this might allow the virus to persist in certain cells of the body. Other research has noted lowered magnesium levels in those with ME. Blood tests can show whether you have or have had one of the viruses likely to trigger ME but even these tests are not infallible and not all are available on the NHS. Blood tests can also check magnesium levels and exclude other serious illnesses that could be responsible for your symptoms.

Blood tests in no way predict the course of your illness, which may be in months or years. Many people make a complete recovery, even after a long illness, while others may have times of remission and relapse continuing over many years.

## PROBLEMS OF LONG ILLNESS

It is hard being ill for two years; it is even harder if you look all right and yet feel awful. When there is no lump to see and other drama that comes with a life-threatening illness is lacking, friends may abandon you after making you feel a fraud.

Not surprisingly anger, guilt, depression and anxiety may accompany your illness. All these combine with the effects of the virus to leave you exhausted, and all are emotions we face when coping with any kind of loss. For you this might include loss of health, career, financial independence, motivation and, to some extent, mobility.

### Anger
You certainly do not come over as angry and yet anger may well be tucked away and be contributing to depression. Anger would be an understandable expression of frustration and protest.

### Guilt
Anger may be targeted at yourself in the form of self-blame. Inappropriately you may feel responsible for your illness and take on feelings of guilt which are reinforced by the pressure of praying friends who need you to be well.

21

## Depression

Depression here is often partly due to altered levels of neurotransmitters caused by the virus. It is also part of a grief for all that has been lost over the past two years. Your aching body will constantly be reminding you of your prison of ill-health, your limbo of exhaustion.

## Anxiety

Anxiety inevitably surrounds the uncertainty of the course of your illness and whether 'the doctors really know what they are doing'. Your security may seem threatened on all sides.

# TALKING TO YOUR DOCTOR

*You say your doctor never really has time to talk.*
You could try to find ways which help communication with your doctor. You are fortunate in that your doctor is not antagonistic to the ME diagnosis. Treatment for, and management of ME are open to widely differing opinions, but clinical experience suggests that early appropriate management can prevent or reduce long-term disability for many people. Why not write down any questions you have so that your doctor or consultant sees that you mean business. It will also ensure that your mind does not blank out at the wrong moment. We suggest you listen to your GP or consultant. If you seek too many opinions you won't know which way to go.

Your doctor clearly does not have enough time to listen to all your worries. Can you try to find someone (your doctor or minister may be able to suggest a person) who does have the time and the skill to listen to you? It does not need to be a highly trained counsellor. Someone trained by a group like Christian Listeners would be particularly appropriate.

It needs someone who is prepared to accept you as you are

without judging your situation in any way. As they listen to you and share your pain, your mind will find space to untangle your thoughts, concerns and relationships.

We would suggest short but regular listening slots. Talking for too long may tire you and become counterproductive – forty-five minutes might be a good maximum. Regular times are good so that you know they are coming. This will help you to 'store' issues or questions as they arise, keeping them on 'hold' until your next listening session. Arranged appointments also take the steam out of pressures as they start to arise. Waiting until you are really desperate and then ringing someone to talk to is far less satisfactory.

## UNRELEASED FEELINGS

ME sometimes affects those prone to some level of depression already. As you share with your listener it may be worth looking back on earlier strains and stresses in your life which may be exacerbating the exhaustion. Repressed feelings, especially anger, can sap energy, and sometimes unreleased feelings become 'symptomatized'. A trained listener will help you to become aware of feelings you may have lost touch with.

ME also affects many high achievers and previously active people. If this applies to you, take note that ME as an illness 'mocks' those who have most prized their performance and activity. It may, therefore, be infinitely valuable to talk out the area of becoming more of a human 'being' and less of a human 'doing'!

Milton wrote in his blindness, 'They also serve who only stand and wait.' Anyone with a fatigue illness has to come to terms at some level with inactivity and reduced output.

If you have been more fulfilled by what you do 'for' others and 'for' God than by what you are, then you may be able to grow *through* this ME condition. This will happen by detecting the roots of your dependence upon activity and finding your true significance as a child of the Father. 'This is my beloved Son with whom I am well pleased' (Matthew 3:17) came *before* Jesus did any of his great works.

## A DANGER FACED

*You say you feel you are slipping into being centred on your illness which is in danger of becoming your identity.*

It is good that you are aware of this danger. May we suggest some lines of approach:

### Acceptance

This may seem a contradiction. But it is only when we accept something that we can let go of it and get on with the rest of our life. An important way ahead for you lies in accepting the troubled waters of your illness and not frantically reaching our for every lifebelt of alternative treatment that well-meaning friends attempt to throw in your direction. Letting go and going along with your illness is not the same as giving up.

### Sanity

Try *not* to become obsessively anxious, e.g. about your diet or your energy output. This can happen with ME sufferers because food allergy may be a factor and because bouts of extra fatigue may follow surges of increased activity. If you allow this kind of consideration to take centre stage then the illness is in danger of becoming your identity.

### Relationships

Stay normal! Keep plenty of friends who don't have ME. Relationships may well be a strain because you are not easy to live with and because you find people tiring. But hold on to some normal social interaction. Keep up with realistic hobbies and enjoyments.

### Your real identity

This is in God alone. Pray that it will be strengthened even in the wilderness place you are in. Worship with others may be difficult or stressful. This is where short, quiet, liturgical services come into their own. (So often when we are really sick we cannot take the praise service where all the 'healings' take place). Use the sacraments.

*Anointing with oil* can be a means for God to separate 'us' from our infirmity. The oil of the Spirit seals us in our true identity in Christ.

Receive the *holy communion* as the sustaining strength of Christ within you. 'Into your life his power breaks through.'

*Use simple prayers.* If you have the gift of tongues it will help you to release feelings from deep within. Use your exhaustion as a prayer, a travailing and groaning with sighs too deep for words (Romans 8:26). If your mind is too clouded to form intelligent phrases, simply repeat the name of 'Jesus' over and over again.


## NO EASY ANSWERS

It is particularly true of your condition that there are no easy answers. Some of what we have said is quite likely to make you feel angry or misunderstood. Many people, especially convinced Christians, can give you an answer to your question which then loads you up with even more anger, guilt and condemnation. You then feel the 'failure' as yours. So we would humbly say that if what we have offered gives you any assistance, that is good; if not, let the failure be ours.

If you need a Christian Listener for yourself, contact Acorn Christian Healing Trust. Tel: 01420 478121.

# 4 Breast Cancer: Facing Truth and Uncertainty

**Q** Six months ago I discovered a lump in my breast and was eventually admitted to hospital for mastectomy. I have had radiotherapy and am taking tablets to prevent a recurrence. The doctor at the hospital said the cancer was all gone. My own doctor says everything is fine, but I am not reassured by this.

My friends at church say I can claim the Lord's healing. I find it difficult to confide in my vicar who never has any time. Half of me wants someone to tell me how often and when the breast cancer recurs, but the other half is frightened to ask. I think I would rather know what I may have to face – does this show a lack of faith?

**A** You raise at least three concerns.

**You are asking if you can know the truth about your condition and what may happen to you.**
It is good to read that all the tumour has been removed and that the doctors are encouragingly hopeful that this is the end of your nightmare. Your feelings of uncertainty are very understandable at this stage. The follow-up you receive at the hospital will be thorough and will help you to believe that you are entirely well.

Medically, you or other readers may be interested to know that the treatment for breast cancer is improving all the time. Although the incidence of this disease is increasing in all countries where statistics are available, the number of people dying from breast cancer has remained stable or increased only slightly.

(It may not be long before a new test is available to predict whether any particular breast cancer is likely to spread. Researchers have found that the cancers likely to spread contain a complex sugar within them which the body does not recognize as abnormal. It is conceivable that a vaccine may be produced which will alert the body's immune system that this sugar is abnormal and so prevent the cancer spreading.)

As you suggest, it is usually far better to know the truth about your illness so that you are aware of what you are up against. Certainly 'false optimism is a potent destroyer of hope.' Having said that, the statistics that you seem to be half asking us to give you would not be particularly helpful to you.

Statistics are not always the most reliable indicators. You can be hemmed in by them, as for example when a time limit is put upon your life. This can be a powerful negative influence. The truth is that the days of our life are not numbered by the doctor but are written in the Lord's 'book' (Psalm 139:16).

Implicit in your question is the feeling that you want to know what will happen to you. It is not possible to know this, and part of the painful growth you are going through is coming to terms with *uncertainty*. This has a lot to do with the true nature of faith which we address below.

Your friends at church and your vicar will not necessarily be able to support you fully in your current feelings. It may therefore be of help to you to join a support or self-help group organized by your hospital. If they don't organize groups write to one of the addresses at the end of this article.

In a group like this, sharing with others in similar circumstances, your loss and uncertainty will be fully understood. You may feel that seeking the help of a group which is not explicitly Christian is a sign of failure. We would encourage you along the lines that human solidarity is God-given. Your faith and love for Christ is in no way negated by seeking help of this kind.

We would hope that you can discover a new way of living richly, trusting God for each day that comes. When Gareth was two, his mother had breast cancer that was found to have spread to the lymph glands and there was no suitable chemotherapy in those days. Her prayer was that she would live until he, the youngest of the family, had grown up. This prayer was answered and she lived life to the full, eventually dying of the disease twenty-one years to the day after her first operation.

**Your friends at church advise you to 'claim the Lord's healing' and your vicar is difficult to confide in.**
Sometimes our expectations of our church fellowship can be unreasonably high. They are only human beings like us! Hopefully, getting some specialist help from a support group as we have suggested will enable you to be more understanding of your church's limitations.

Clearly several members of the church are struggling to come to terms with what 'healing' means. Advising you to 'claim the Lord's healing' is not helpful for you and we are sorry that it puts you under pressure.

We have to confess that often the suffering members of a church suffer even more at the hands of healing enthusiasts who have no theology of suffering. It is an unbalanced and immature approach which leads to their insistence on the Lord's healing as *cure*.

The true salvation-healing which Christians believe in, is far wider than simple physical cure: it embraces for example living with suffering as well as the 'ultimate healing' of our dying in the Lord's care. May we suggest that:

- *You talk to someone in leadership in your church.*
You could ask the vicar to give you an appointment, or you may prefer to seek out another respected 'elder' of the church. Explain your predicament to them. This will enable you to feel more understood, and hopefully they may know an appropriate 'niche' for you. It may be a particular home group or a friendship circle where others can accept you and offer genuine love and understanding.
- *You see yourself as an opportunity rather than a problem.*
This may be hard for you but we can see that you are in reality a gift. You are a gift to your church and a means by which members could grow in maturity as they learn to accept you as you are rather than how they would prefer you to be! We realize this is not easy but we encourage you to stick with them if you possibly can. They need you.

**You raise the issue of what it means to live by faith.**

Often when we look at serious illness we seem to suggest only two alternatives. One is to be completely healed in a physical sense, the other is a certain downhill slide to death. You are anxious to know which alternative you face. Implicit in all this is a sense of *certainty*: you want to be certain either that you will live ('healed by faith'?) or that you will die (not healed by faith?).

The reality is that faith is *never* about certainty in terms of what we can expect to happen to us. Faith *is* about living with uncertainty. We 'walk by faith and not by sight' (2 Corinthians 5:7). Our faith is in the *Lord* and not in the supposed certainty of what he does. In the words of the old prayer – 'We who are wearied by the changes and chances of this fleeting world repose in your eternal changelessness.' He himself is the only certainty.

All of us, whether we have cancer or not, actually live with uncertainty, with 'the changes and chances of this fleeting world'. What your illness is doing is highlighting for you that uncertainty which is a part of all human life.

By coming to terms with the uncertainties of your illness you have a real opportunity to step out in faith in ways you never did before.

We sense in your question a real courage with which to face the truth. We pray that God will give you the courage to be able to embrace the truth which is uncertainty and to be able to embrace him also within it.

*Addresses:*   Breast Care and Mastectomy Association, 26A Harrison Street, King's Cross, London WC1 8IG.
BACUP, 3 Bath Place, Rivington Street, London EC2A 3JR.

# 5 When a Loved One Dies

**Q** My father is very ill and will not live many months. When he dies what would you advise for all the family about seeing him after death?

**A** When he dies some or all of you may be present. You cannot actually plan this although it is good to work out some kind of strategy beforehand.

We see various responses to this when people die at Burrswood. Sometimes the family can bear to visit only for a few moments at a time, and the actual moment of death is too painful for them to contemplate. Others arrange a vigil in relays. Others stay together as a family group for as much of the time as possible right up to the end.

Although it is good to say goodbyes, this does not usually happen very tidily and there are probably very few perfectly planned deaths. Let your children do what they really want to, which may well include visiting their grandfather when he is dying.

Sadly, the hardest thing for many is to share their feelings with their children. In fact the children can bear it better than we think. It has been said that children can live through anything so long as they are told the truth and are allowed to share with loved ones the natural feelings that come with suffering. This applies to everything we say on this subject, including viewing the body after death.

If a child is kept from experiencing things like dying and funerals, these then become more frightening. 'What awful things must go on,' they ask, 'if I couldn't be allowed to share in it?'

As the moment of death approaches, try not to hold on to your father too tightly. Simply be alongside him, and in your actions, your thoughts and your prayers, be releasing him to go on his journey.

Dying is usually peaceful.

Your father may or may not be aware of your presence. He may have a 'bubbly-sounding' chest and breathing difficulties that you will be very aware of and yet he will not. Generally, at this stage, the medication given and the lack of oxygen to the brain will distance him from any physical distress.

### Prayer

You can be praying that the Lord will come to him, that he may be released from fear or guilt or anything that ties him to this world, and that he may be drawn into the beauty of God's presence.

It is both agonizing and beautiful to be in the room with someone who is dying. It is like standing with him or her on the threshold of eternity.

You may want a chaplain or your minister to pray with your father during the days and hours leading up to his death, and at the moment of death or soon after. It may be worth arranging this beforehand so that your minister knows what you want.

Here at Burrswood we pray along the lines already suggested, often using anointing with oil. At the moment of death or soon after we usually anoint a person for the last time. This can be regarded as a *sealing* of the physical process. We are saying, 'You gave him to us, Lord, now we give him back to you.' Prayers of 'commendation' are also used: 'Go forth upon your journey from this world, O Christian soul, in the peace of him in whom you have believed . . .'

It is also quite natural to speak *to* our departed loved ones – words of love, apology, farewell. This need not be confused with spiritualism, or 'calling up the dead'. It is a way of praying which helps to express what may still be unresolved in us.

### After death

This is an important time and we recommend that you don't rush off. The practicalities of sorting things out may help to occupy you, but if you can, it will help you to stay around his body for a while. The only time we might be cautious about recommending viewing the body is when severe disfigurement has occurred. If you are nervous, ask someone to explain what you will see – a chaplain, doctor, or nurse will almost certainly be willing to accompany you. Their presence can be calming and make the experience 'safe'.

Viewing the body after death will vary according to the setting. Circumstances will be different in your own home or somewhere geared to the dying process like Burrswood or a hospice. A busy hospital may be more focused on the living, and we have heard of distress caused by the thoughtlessness of presentation in hospital mortuaries.

Again, there is a great difference between seeing someone straight after death, when they may simply appear to have fallen asleep, and seeing them at a later stage which may well be in a 'chapel of rest'.

To see your father at an undertakers' may well seem more of an ordeal. The surroundings somehow speak of death, the atmosphere seems colder (literally), his body will be cold and the whole scene may feel eerie. If you were not able to be present when he died, we would suggest that it may help you to see him at the undertakers'. You can be guided by your own feelings here.

### Staying with the dead

The period between death and burial should not be regarded as a non-event. We have the very best example in Luke 23:53-24:1. It was once common in our own culture to have the body in the house before the funeral. This still happens in many countries.

Far from being morbid, staying with the dead can be a healing vigil. Nobody says the women were morbid to come with spices to the tomb: they loved Jesus. In Zefferelli's TV film *Jesus of Nazareth*, made in the 1970s, one of the most moving scenes is when Jesus is taken down lovingly from the cross to the accompaniment of laments and weeping.

## A TIME OF HEALING

At Burrswood we find the hours after death are a time when personal and corporate healing takes place. A conversation can go on *around* a body that could not take place without it! David was once reflecting on this with a Baptist minister on placement with us. We were in a room where a person lay dead. The minister described how, when his young daughter died, the nurses allowed him to carry her body to the mortuary chapel. This he said 'cracked him up' but was something wonderful he would never forget. As he walked away from the hospital that day, he 'heard' his daughter say, 'You see, Jesus did heal me, Daddy.'

Gareth remembers the privilege of helping to wash down and tidy up his father soon after he died. There is a sub-Christian view which says Christians should not 'stay with' the dead. We should *either* remember them 'as they were' *or* we should think 'they're not really here, they're in heaven.' The difficulty with both of these responses is that they evade the pain and the love of the human farewell to which the dead body allows us to give full expression. We need to move *through* the stages of grief (see Chapter 13). There is no way *round*, and avoiding the reality of the corpse will not help us.

*We realize that our thoughts may have provoked some disturbance, especially perhaps for those unable for whatever reason to be with their departed loved ones at the time of death. We suggest that for you it may be a help to your work of grief if you confide in a trusted friend or counsellor.*

It is a natural human love response to want to spend some moments with our dead. We are glad that you have posed this important question. God bless you as you stay with the process of dying in order to know more of the reality of the resurrection.

# 6 Alternative Therapies and the New Age

Q So many people come to me asking for Christian guidelines as to the use of 'alternative' therapies. Please can you help? Why are so many people paying for alternative therapies when orthodox medical care can be free?

## A The limits of Western medicine

Western medicine has been criticized in recent years, both from within and from outside the medical profession.

Perhaps it was Ivan Illich (*Limits to Medicine*, 1976) who sounded the warning bells. 'The medical establishment has become a major threat to health' is how the introduction to his book begins, with the heading in chapter one, 'Doctors' effectiveness – an illusion.'

There has been pressure for more patient-centred care and a model of ill health that goes beyond consideration of disease processes. It is in this climate that the demand for 'alternative therapies' has grown.

During his term as President of the British Medical Association, the Prince of Wales urged the Association to look critically at Western medicine. He suggested that 'today's unorthodoxy is probably going to be tomorrow's convention'.

### The attraction of alternative therapies

People with chronic ill-defined health problems who have gained no diagnostic label may find that they receive little constructive medical help once serious organic illness has been excluded. Not surprisingly those who are longing to be well, finding their symptoms are disbelieved, look elsewhere.

Alternative therapies may offer attractive explanations as to the causes of illness, explanations which Western medicine would describe as fanciful. Alternative practitioners are seen to offer the patient:

- the use of 'natural' treatments as opposed to unnatural medications
- time and a listening ear
- touch, compassion and understanding
- an unquestioning acceptance of the reality of their symptoms
- a feeling of being left in control of their treatment (for instance in managing a special diet).

The question of payment which you raise may also be viewed constructively since people literally invest in what they pay for.

All these seeming benefits serve to emphasize common weaknesses in Western medical care. But what begins as a journey of hope often turns out to be another cul-de-sac. Turning away from the symptom-relieving, disease-orientated approach of orthodoxy towards one which purports to be natural, energy-balancing and holistic may not provide the way through. Indeed this brings its own rigidity and bondage to unnecessary treatments, diets and the like.

## RECOGNIZING STRENGTHS

At the same time, dangers and cautions should not lead to the rejection, out of hand, of all alternative therapies. Indeed, many advances in Western medicine have come from abandoning incorrect traditional dogma and by considering 'alternative therapies'! Many herbal treatments have been found to contain compounds that are recognized as effective in treating disease.

As Christians we want to recognize the limits of a scientific medical approach. We want to stress the need in health care to consider the 'whole person', which includes the overlapping areas of psychological, emotional and spiritual wellbeing.

We want to affirm, as do many of the alternative therapies, the importance of living naturally and relating rightly to the environment around us.

## UNDERSTANDING CONCEPTS

Underlying many of the alternative therapies are what we may broadly call 'New Age' concepts. These are incredibly complex and we in no way regard ourselves as specialists here. Put simply, in our culture the folk religion of the day has moved from one that was basically Christian to a much wider view.

Defining New Age beliefs is rather like defining a mist. It is as if bits and pieces of all religions and none are allowed to flow together. In particular we might point out:

**The move from an objective sense of 'God as other' towards a subjective sense of 'God' or even 'Christ' in all of us and in all matter.**

This is like a return to aspects of pantheism and paganism. It may at times seem close to (Christian) creation theology. As so often happens, truth and falsehood are perilously close. Christians worshipping the Creator in and through his creation are not doing the same as those who seek healing power from crystals, for example (see Romans 1:25).

**The concepts of 'energy' and 'power' which often underlie alternative therapies.**

Disease is seen to result from an unbalanced flow of universal energy. Healers are those who in some way channel the energies and powers required to bring back the balance.

There may be something illuminating in this concept. But it is not Christian to seek energy in the sense of 'having' power or 'giving' it to someone else. In that sense Christians can never be 'healers'. We are interested only in the energizing work of the Holy Spirit 'who proceeds from the Father and the Son' (Nicene Creed).

**The way alternative therapies often 'cluster' with dangerous spiritual beliefs and practices.**

We can compare this to the drug culture. Smoking cannabis may indeed be virtually harmless and even preferable to drinking alcohol. But if you get into a culture where cannabis is smoked you are likely to get drawn into something else which is really dangerous.

Similarly, you may go to a health food shop and become interested in aromatherapy or reflexology – the 'soft' end of the market, although some Christians would take a hard line here. But culturally those kinds of activities cluster together with things like astrology and 'spiritual healing' as it is called today. 'Spiritual healing' is often a fashionable front for spiritualistic/mediumistic practice. The latter always leads, in our experience, to some kind of oppression or bondage.

**Erosion of distinctively Christian teaching about Jesus – now seen as one of the prophets or great masters – and his death and resurrection.**

Reincarnation is a popular concept among New Agers.

We need to realize how widespread and respectable New Age concepts are becoming. It is quite normal, for example, for the health-care world to turn to alternative practitioners and spiritual healers when the need is felt to address areas beyond the physical and the organic. Mainstream Christian belief and practice has lost what grip it had on common thinking.

The question asks for Christian guidelines. These cannot be simplistic and we would counsel against outright rejection of all alternative approaches. Christians have different views about how and where to draw boundaries. Honest evaluation of alternative medical therapies must involve a real disregard for previous prejudice.

Alternative therapies claiming to be complete systems of healing need close examination:

## CHRISTIAN GUIDELINES

* Do the claims made for the therapy fit the facts?
* Does the method, diagnosis and treatment have roots or current practices related to the occult? (see Matthew 7:15-19).
* Has the therapy been subjected to unprejudiced reliable and scientific assessment? Anecdotal reports should be disregarded.
* Is the religious belief of the 'alternative' practitioner interwoven

into the methodology; are 'energy forces' involved in the alternative therapy?

- Prayer is the first stop for any Christian who is sick. Healing and wholeness come from God himself by the power of the Holy Spirit and through the body of Christ – his church. Does the therapy in any way deny this truth?

## SOME NO-GO AREAS

In our understanding, involvement here means putting oneself into the grip of powers contrary to the Holy Spirit. We would include blatant Satanism and all forms of witchcraft, together with 'spiritual healing' which is allied to spiritualism (sometimes called 'spiritism').

Psychic or natural healing, where healers seem to have inherited or acquired abilities without asking for them, we would also put in the no-go area. The argument against this tends to say, 'Surely all power for good comes from God?' Our response would be that power *over* others or power to *see into* others' lives is not an ability God wishes human beings to have.

In advising those who feel they have inherited psychic powers (quite a common situation in our experience) we would encourage them to give their powers 'back' to the Lord Jesus.

This usually leads to a new freedom and joy. It is important to notice the similarity between psychic abilities like foresight and the gifts of the Holy Spirit as listed in 1 Corinthians 12. We would not, however, understand them as the same. The gifts of the Holy Spirit really belong to the Spirit and are given to us as we have need of them.

## REDEEMABLE AREAS

There is a 'grey area' in between the no-go areas and the 'word and sacrament' life of the church of Jesus. We would put here all medical practice and the use of secular counselling therapies. What we can legitimately bring about under the Lordship of Jesus is thereby redeemable.

We would suggest it is often important to assess the practitioner, particularly if we are putting deep parts of ourselves into their hands, as in hypnotism. We need to ask, 'What drives them?'

Christians have different views in the grey areas. Some regard yoga and acupuncture, for example, as no-go places, because the Eastern religious base is opposed to the Lordship of Christ. We have sympathy with this view but we also know about 'Christian yoga' and Christian acupuncturists, where the practitioners have thought through their position and are clearly centred on 'God in Jesus'.

## SPIRITUAL VIGILANCE

We do nobody a service by knee-jerk reactions which brand everything faintly suspicious as occult or demonic. Clearly this is a spiritual minefield and the powers of evil will use it for their own ends. Remember that the devil is described as a wily schemer (Ephesians 6:11) with destructive ambitions (1 Peter 5:8), and that signs and wonders may be counterfeit (2 Thessalonians 2:9).

It is good to recognize, however, that the normal teaching about spiritual protection and spiritual warfare applies in this area. That is to say, Christians are on the winning side and are covered by the protection of God and the blood of Jesus. We can give the devil more power than he has by becoming too intense or defensive.

## SOME MEDICAL NOTES

• Therapies which our Western 'Christian' culture regards as fringe or alternative, would in fact be 'orthodox' and 'traditional' in different cultures.

- Some therapies are hard to assess in an overall way and inevitably end in a 'grey' box of uncertainty and caution.

Unfortunately some non-medically qualified 'alternative' practitioners can still practise homeopathy. They are likely to use this as a total system of medicine. We have encountered a rare situation where the potentized medicines were prepared using pendulum swinging and astrology. Compare this with consulting a Christian doctor who is also qualified in homeopathy. Here the homeopathic remedies are prepared under harmless conditions and strict criteria by a practitioner who also looks to using modern medicines where they are needed.

(Incidentally, with reference to your question, homeopathy is available on the NHS from a few centres in the UK.)

The first instance is seen by some as an example of a true 'alternative therapy' while the second could be called a 'complementary therapy'. Therapies that do not exclude the use of Western medicine are indeed often seen as complementary rather than alternative therapies.

- Some 'alternative' practitioners are qualified doctors but many are not and they are not answerable to the law.
- Where life is at risk, there is no rational alternative to prayer and Western medicine – there are many tragic case histories relating to those who have abandoned orthodox medical care in acute illness.

## THE WAY FORWARD

We believe that the way ahead is for practitioners of orthodox medicine to be allowed the time, within the pressures of the NHS, to treat the whole person. Medical training and teaching are now geared to a multidisciplinary approach with the interrelating of disease processes and physical, mental and spiritual 'dis-ease' being given credibility.

But time needs to be given. If that were the case, would so many seek out alternative treatments, we wonder?

Western medicine does not remove the need for Christian prayer and ministry. But it does make it easier to forget about them for long enough to leave us terrifyingly exposed and not knowing where to turn if, in due course, it fails to bring about a cure.

Christians will want to exercise vigilance as regards those who offer them help and support. But let us at the same time welcome the healing grace of God through Jesus Christ wherever we may find it.

# 7 Are Healing Miracles Witnessed Today?

**Q In view of all the publicity about miracles, I would be grateful for some help. Do you think that miracles of healing are witnessed today?**

**A** The short answer to this has to be 'yes' because God is a God of wonders. We say 'wonders' because the word 'miracle' is based on the Latin *mirari*, meaning 'to wonder at'. In the Bible, the Old Testament words are 'sign' and 'wonder' (as in Deuteronomy 4:34), and the two key New Testament words are *dunamis* (meaning 'act of power', as in dynamite), and *semeion* (meaning sign, as in the miracles of John's Gospel e.g. John 2:11).

Your question is, are miracles of healing witnessed today? Until recently, Protestant orthodoxy has tended towards limiting belief in miracles to those recorded in Scripture. Catholic orthodoxy has accepted miracles at all times in the life of the Church and tended to see these focused around the cult of the saints and their shrines. In the last twenty years, charismatic theology has suggested that we might expect miracles as normative in the life and witness of the Church and John Wimber (e.g. in *Power Evangelism*) challenges the whole cramping Western scientific world view. We find ourselves holding a middle position. We wonder at God's works of power and recognize, therefore, that miracles happen. But we would not want to insist on them as usual to everyday experience.

Clearly the ministry of Jesus and of his apostles was packed full of signs and wonders, demonstrating the breaking in of God's kingdom and pointing like a signpost to faith in the living Lord. But Christ himself warned against an overdependence on signs and resisted performing miracles as some kind of spectator sport.

> I saw signs of divine power, like those of olden days, were frequently occurring in modern times too.
>
> Even now (AD 400) miracles are performed in Christ's name either by his sacrament, or by prayers . . . but they do not enjoy a blaze of publicity.
>
> Miracles performed to make the world believe have not ceased.
>
> *St Augustine*

We would want to regard miracles over the years since the earthly ministry of Jesus – often occurring in waves at particular times and in particular places – as ongoing signs of the breaking in of the kingdom. Because that kingdom is both 'already' and 'not yet' the miraculous signs are not everywhere all the time. Indeed, there would be nothing to 'wonder at' if it was happening all the time.

### Supernatural

There is a more scientific understanding of a miracle as the special intervention of God transcending the normal order of natural laws. This is where we get the concept of something being 'supernatural'. But in reality the natural laws are not some rigid pattern that science lays down for us, because all science is deductive and based upon what has been normally observed to happen.

Often the healing miracles are in this area of something appearing to happen that 'can't' normally happen – e.g. the dead being raised. We would want to say that just because something doesn't normally happen, it doesn't mean it can never happen. Christians are open to the awe and mystery of God at work. We worked at Burrswood always against the backdrop of the great wonder by which Dorothy Kerin was raised from her deathbed in 1912 whilst suffering from tubercular meningitis. To work in that setting, *with* all the apparatus of medical investigation and treatment, was a constant reminder of both the possibility of the miraculous and the need to stay scientifically detached.

### Medical map

You ask specifically about 'miracles of healing'. This raises the important issue of medical verification. So many claims in regard to the healing of medical conditions do not stand up to scientific scrutiny, yet scientific investigation is not free from personal prejudice and supposition. Scientific research papers can often be interpreted in different ways. Specialists struggle enough to make a firm diagnosis with some everyday illnesses. Scans, X-rays, biopsies, blood and biochemical tests all lead to a presumed diagnosis and an accompanying prognosis. It is not hard to get doctors to admit that they can remember diagnoses that have had to be revised when they had seemed certain and proven. The disease process takes an unexpected course and an explanation is needed. A changed diagnosis feels better than to admit that God may have had a hand in things! We tend to see what we want to see. Arrogance can come in on both sides – either by insisting that scientific proof of the disease process is *essential* prior to contemplating the supernatural ways of God, or by insisting that remission or cure is *always* due to the miraculous hand of God. The belief that miracles happen today is not helped by Christians who make exaggerated claims of cure either through misunderstanding, poor communication or a desire to hit the headlines. Distortion of the truth or a lack of understanding of normal disease processes are all too common. On the other hand, we follow a Lord whose miraculous cures are recorded in the Gospels. Medicine is both an art and a science and, unless our mind and eyes are open to what God may do, we will surely miss out on the many 'wonders' of today. Almost inevitably, Christian claims for healing have suffered from inadequate medical documentation. Medical records often omit vital information when it comes to looking back over a 'case history'. Key investigations were not carried out because they were thought costly and unnecessary at the time and so on. Such is the unexpected nature of God's 'wonders' that it is virtually always a matter of looking back and reviewing the evidence rather than looking forward and planning to document fully a miraculous cure that will make history!

At the Roman Catholic shrine of Lourdes in France there has been a medical bureau for more than a century. Of over a thousand cases of physical healing examined between 1918 and 1991, only sixty-four have been accepted by both doctors and priests as undoubted miracles, the last being recorded in 1970. It seems quite likely, with increased medical sophistication, that if the evidence for these was re-examined now, other scientific explanations would be found. But then medical verification is not everything. It can only confirm what has gone on from an observable point of view. Whatever its findings, we shall still find ourselves wondering at the great mystery of God's power at work.

Then again, why be so eager to prove that a physical cure has come about by supernatural rather than medical means? Is not the God of wonders in both? We marvel and wonder at the miracles of modern medicine. It may be helpful to understand medical insight like a map. A map is perfectly true and helpful: it will guide me up a mountain. But it cannot show me what it feels like to stand on top of a mountain and look at a sunset. Similarly, the medical map cannot tell me everything that is going on in the whole of my being.

## Letting go

There is all the difference in the world between believing miracles may happen and creating a pressured expectancy about 'having the faith' to ask God for them. It may well be that true miracles happen rather at the point where we let go of demanding them and get our focus somewhere else. That focus for Christians can never be on the miracle itself but on the person of Our Lord Jesus Christ. So it is important not to become entirely taken up with miracles as simply remarkable physical cures. We believe that the Christian healing ministry should not be focused on the performing of the miraculous but rather on allowing the power and presence of Jesus to transform lives. Now, there is a miracle to be witnessed today!

## Helpful reading
Healing Miracles – a doctor investigates by Rex Gardner (Darton, Longman & Todd)
Miracles by Michael Poole (Scripture Union)

# 8 The Value of Teamwork, Including the Patient

**Q** How does the multidisciplinary team work at Burrswood? Is there any way of getting this kind of care into the wider community? When my vicar visited me in hospital, he obviously had not talked to my doctor.

**A** At Burrswood we are always striving after an ideal of team work which is never quite matched by reality. We try to see each of our patients as a key member of the team, in the hope that nothing is imposed upon them in a 'them and us' fashion.

Our 'inner' team for up to thirty-one patients includes two doctors, two chaplains, a counsellor, two part-time physiotherapists and about twenty-eight nurses, one of whom becomes a key worker for each individual patient.

## INITIAL ENCOUNTERS

In contrast to a normal hospital situation, the team shares one A4 file of notes for each patient. We distinguish between team comments, i.e. the physio writes in red, the counsellor in green and the chaplain uses a blue page. The doctors just write illegibly! The nursing team also uses a daily record. The file contains all referral letters, the patient's own application to Burrswood and the results of all investigations.

One of the nursing team welcomes the patient and makes initial enquiries about his/her daily living activities, medication and expectation. The duty doctor then meets the new arrival, explains the nature of the file and mentions that the patient can see and be taken through the contents of their record at any time; in reality this virtually never happens, as patients feel safe in the team's holding.

## CONFIDENTIALITY

The feeling of safety is enhanced by a routine explanation of the boundaries of confidentiality. It is explained that whatever is shared by the patient with any member of the team will be the property of the team, but that the team as a whole is a totally confidential group.

If a patient shares something with a team member, then the patient only has to say, 'Keep that to yourself.' The 'restricted information' is not recorded in writing nor passed on verbally. This 'team confidentiality' brings its own sense of security and confidence.

## DAILY REPORT

At present there is only one full team meeting a week but on other weekdays the meeting has a particular emphasis, e.g. concentration on new admissions or those in one area of the medical centre. It is difficult to strike the balance so that team meetings do not take up the whole day!

The team also meet on a daily basis to discuss all proposed new admissions. Bringing the team together in this way is fundamental to our work but is costly in every sense.

## THE WIDER TEAM

Your question focuses on the doctor/pastor relationship. Nonetheless this 'inner' team could not function effectively without the 'outer' team, which includes all community members – the house and kitchen team, receptionists, secretaries, the pool team, estate team, volunteers, administrators, those given to prayer and so on.

Caring is stressful and teamwork is time-consuming. Sometimes it seems easier just to get on by yourself, but the strength is that stress is diffused among the team members. Interdisciplinary and personal support is never far away.

At all times the team has to work at maintaining communication and being ready to acknowledge and handle conflict. The pain that is triggered in us by our intensive care of others in pain needs to be handled. The team must be supported, receive input and be open to audit.

At Burrswood the approach of each discipline has decidedly fuzzy edges because we have a common calling. Thus the chaplain may point the way for medical insight, the counsellor may suggest massage from the physiotherapist, the nurse may hear the key that unlocks the door of pain, the physio may be praying and laying on therapeutic hands, while the doctor is often seen anointing with oil and laying on hands with prayer. No team member is ever 'going it alone' but remains part of the whole.

## DISCIPLINARY INTERFACES

Much of the creative tension of teamwork arises from the differences in training and approach that tend to belong to the different disciplines.

For example, the nursing discipline tends to want to make things better, while the counselling discipline aims to stay with pain. So a typical scenario at midday is the chaplain or counsellor saying to the senior nurse, 'Mr X will need lunch in his room after a heavy session with me.' To which the reply comes, 'You've done it again, just when we were getting him better!'

We need to hear each other so that counselling does not simply stir things up for the sake of it and nursing does not always simply smooth things over.

One of the fascinating interfaces is with the physio/hydrotherapy department. Recently someone's treatment involved 'letting go in the water', which carried strong sacramental and baptismal overtones.

The use of liturgy and symbolism has an important interface with counselling work. This includes both fixed events like a daily eucharist and services with laying on of hands, and also spontaneously arranged events for individual situations like the 'burning' of sins and resentments or the use of holy water to bring cleansing.

We are always working at the interface of prayer and counselling. Sometimes 'therapy' goes round in circles and we need prayer to move us on. We need the intervention of the Holy Spirit beyond human resources.

At other times the opposite is true. There may have been an over-reliance on prayer ministry leading to overspiritualizing. Unwanted personal material may get projected on to the devil – to be cast out, please! Or we avoid doing our own work by always hoping the Lord will come in and do it for us.

At such times we often need the human encounter of the counselling discipline which will not run away from focusing on ourselves, in order to engage our personal resources.

Crucial to all our teamwork is the interface of the medical and spiritual. We are most unhappy that so much deliverance work, for example, is undertaken without medical support or insight, especially when there is a history of mental illness.

Again there are creative tensions. A doctor can expect a certain immediacy of treatment about which a pastor may be more wary. It may be implied, for example, that the chaplain should 'do something about their need for forgiveness', if possible by tomorrow, as if it were an injection to be administered.

A spiritual response is needed to medical diagnosis and prognosis so that these do not become all-controlling. This is a very difficult balance to keep.

Hierarchies are interesting here. Is the hospital consultant 'god'? At Burrswood he may find himself waiting for the chaplain – or even, on one occasion, a Greek Orthodox bishop – to vacate a patient's room. It would be a totally different story in hospital.

We are blessed by consultants who are available to us (including a consultant psychiatrist) who can identify with this way of working and who understand the benefits of balancing spiritual input alongside the medical.

'Report' also has its humorous moments at the medical/spiritual interface, e.g. 'His inspiration is poor' probably means he's not good at breathing in. And is 'pneumatology' about understanding the lungs . . . or the Holy Spirit . . . or perhaps both?

The joys and difficulties of real communication developing into mutual respect for each other's contribution underlie the talking that you so much want your vicar to undertake with your doctor.

## CARE IN THE WIDER COMMUNITY

It has been said that authentic teamwork requires a group of people who
— *possess individual expertise*
— *are responsible for making individual decisions*
— *hold a common purpose*
— *meet to communicate, share and consolidate knowledge*
— *establish agreed goals*
— *integrate care plans*
— *are committed to their own and each other's personal growth*

It seems to us that initiatives in team care often have to start with the individual in need. You may yourself be the key to unlocking the professional doors of confidentiality and to building trust into areas of mistrust.

The doctors can be given the confidence to think that the pastor handling life and death issues will not be like a bull in a china shop and vice versa. Each professional needs motivating to invest time in communication for the good of the individual.

The primary health care team based on a general practitioner has to be encouraged to take on board other relevant carers for each individual's situation.

The Macmillan nurse bringing expertise to the care of the dying can, with motivation on all sides, be successfully incorporated within the team to allow a constructive interchange of ideas and information.

The pastor, the skilled listener, the practical neighbour, the home help, the volunteer driver, the school nurse or whoever, can be drawn into the circle of the health care team. But, we think, the permission, encouragement and initial suggestion may have to come from the patient.

## INITIATIVES BY THE DOCTOR

The Christian general practitioner can 'oil the wheels' of pastoral communication when he/she knows that the patient is a church member. In asking the patient whether he/she minds the situation being discussed with the priest, the GP has to take great care. The sick person might immediately wrongly think that his/her illness was one of 'grave concern' – literally!

We know of one GP who held a joint surgery each week with her minister – she was examining and prescribing while the priest in another consulting room laid on hands in the name of Christ.

It can also be all too easy to allow spiritual care to drift into areas of 'faith-healing' or 'spiritual healing' other than Christian prayer unless the input is from under the umbrella of a Christian church offered by members of the body of Christ.

## INITIATIVES BY THE PASTOR

The priest or minister can do a number of practical things to

encourage medicine and Christianity to work together. He can:
— make a point of getting to know local GPs
— enter into an agreed partnership with a doctor, as in the apostolate of the Acorn Christian Healing Trust
— make the most of St Luke's-tide by inviting them to a special service with a sermon topic of interest to them, perhaps an issue of medical ethics. The most successful church at doing this attracts ninety doctors to such a service – perhaps it was the mention of sherry afterwards that did the trick!
— have a telephone in the church foyer for doctors coming to a service to answer bleeps
— have pastoral/prayer group support for those in the caring professions and not just for the sick
— encourage key members of the congregation to train in Christian Listening (details from Acorn Christian Healing Trust, Whitehill Chase) and to make their skills known to local doctors
— make the practical services offered via the church office known to local practices, e.g. people who will shop for, sit with, befriend, take patients to hospital appointments
— ensure that the congregation learns to act in pastorally responsible ways. Many caring professionals like GPs distrust church groups where well-meaning enthusiasts can wreak havoc in fragile people who need handling with care.

## CONCLUSION

We offer our example of teamwork at Burrswood as one model which is still evolving. The work of each person caring for the one who is sick will always be specific and individual but needs to be done in concert with others.

Christian discipleship has always been about teamwork ever since Jesus sent us out 'two by two' – not to be 'prima donnas'. In practical terms, duplication is avoided, communication is clearer.

For you personally there is also something to do. Next time you have visits from your doctor and your vicar, grasp the nettle, take the initiative and break down the walls of confidentiality by asking them to get together.

The effect of this may not be felt just by you; you may be encouraging a more caring community to be born!

# 9 The Urge to Keep On Eating

**Q** I have times when I cannot stop eating. Strangely, in the past, I have struggled to eat at all. Eating has now become compulsive and my church friends suggest that I may need deliverance ministry. I feel unhappy about this in that I have never been involved with the occult. Your advice please.

**A** Your question is specifically about eating but is relevant to the whole area of addiction and dependency.

We all have our favourite addictions to which we turn when we are under stress. For you it is food, while for others it can range from chemical substances to spending money or constant contact with others in order to avoid alone-ness.

The main emphasis of our response to you is to encourage you not to concentrate on the addiction itself but on the underlying needs that drive you to the pantry or fridge.

We suggest you do not just focus on the issue of food intake. Rather, try to unravel the difficulties and deprivations that have led to compulsive eating.

Incidentally, compulsive eating is not simply greed, although you may continually berate yourself for your greed. A compulsive eater may well, for example, exercise an iron control over other areas of life and be very disciplined over things that cause other people problems, like the use of time and money.

*You may find these questions helpful to ask yourself.*

**Are you using food as a tranquillizer?** From infancy you will have equated fullness with contentment.

Did you know that the brain releases endorphins after a large meal? These are the body's natural pain-killers and relaxants.

We can get 'hooked' on the good feelings they give us. Maybe when you cried as a child you were 'shut up' and pacified with food.

**Are you using food to suppress uncomfortable feelings?** Are you, literally, stuffing them down?

As Christians, we are often taught that we should be full of joy and peace and that we shouldn't be angry or sad. So we deny or suppress unacceptable feelings. We try to block them out.

Is it easier to focus on food than on your problems; to 'fill yourself up' so there's no room for anything else?

**Or is food a way of filling up the emptiness within you?** You may be aware of an aching void within you that needs satisfaction. Boredom, unfulfilment, and frustration can all drive you to food.

**Is loving food safer than loving people?** By adding to your weight do you feel that you will make yourself less attractive and protect yourself from love and intimacy?

The opposite of this (to which you refer when you say you previously struggled to eat at all) is – do you keep underweight in order to inhibit the shapeliness of your body?

**Can you identify any triggers?** If you think back to when the current intensity of eating began you may be able to see some immediate trigger. It is worth locating this in order to be aware of the hurts or stresses in your life that press the food buttons.

## BREAKING THE CYCLE

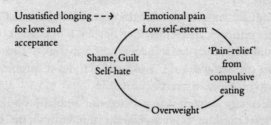

Unsatisfied longing - - → Emotional pain
for love and     Low self-esteem
acceptance

Shame, Guilt     'Pain-relief'
Self-hate     from
compulsive
eating

Overweight

*In order to break into this cycle, Helena Wilkinson, consultant to Anorexia and Bulimia Care, identifies three areas you may well need to look at with someone skilled enough to help you.*

1 *Self worth* – which is crucial to your identity as a person. How you value yourself is closely linked to what others think about you – or more often what you think they think!

How you perceive yourself will also be centred around what you feel about your body. Food addiction is an abuse of your body which is saying something about yourself. Your self-esteem may swing with whether you have been compulsively eating or not.

2 *Sexuality* – you do not say whether you are a man or a woman. Eating disorders are much more observable in women but are not confined to them. We have already implied that compulsion eating may be warding off sexual feelings we would rather not stay with. For example, the pain of sexual abuse may be contained in some way by eating. Feelings of rage, fear and shame may be numbed in this way.

The food problem can also distract carers from the real issue. This is an area that requires sensitive and careful handling. When you find a helper you can trust, it may be something you can look at together.

3 *Family background* – our inner pain arises from the circumstances of our own story. It may be, for example, that your parents found it difficult to face their own emotional needs and effectively blocked you from expressing yours.

Once again, a sensitive and skilled helper may enable you to face the issues in your family background that may have led to compulsive eating.

### Deliverance

Your friends are suggesting something called 'deliverance ministry' and you are unhappy about this. First of all, it is important to find the friends who will really help and support you and not load you up with more stresses and guilt. Every church has its problem-solvers who swoop on those in overt need.

What seems to happen is that when the problems do not resolve easily we start to think 'this is so bad that it must be an evil bondage'.

Our general response to your question here is *yes*, openness in prayer to the Lord who delivers us from evil is important. But *no*, it will not be the whole answer. There is no way of avoiding the struggle of living with ourselves and we fear that your friends may be hoping for an easy way out.

While fully recognizing the scriptural authority for deliverance ministry, we would like to say something about styles of this work, in case your friends have something specific in mind.

Those who offer a highly explicit deliverance ministry usually operate according to problem-solving techniques, i.e. in order to 'deal with' the evil spirits they need a 'word of knowledge' (or spiritual insight) to know specifically what these spirits are. They then feel able to address these spirits by name and command them to leave by the authority of Jesus Christ.

This is the style of 'charismatic deliverance ministry' that has developed over the last twenty-five years. It sometimes operates with dubious authority and can be little more than a gathering of well-meaning enthusiasts.

If you go for such help you are putting yourself into fairly directive hands. You will be ministered to 'as the Spirit leads', which may feel as if you get little choice but to obey. Although this is not our own style, we recognize that some people are helped by it.

We suggest that you need to feel fairly strong in yourself to submit to this style of ministry. As with all 'power' approaches, it carries the risk that some people are left shattered or confused.

If you do engage with such ministries, check out that they have some proper church authority to which they are accountable, and make sure you also have supportive Christian friends who are sane and balanced, with a good sense of humour and their feet firmly on the ground.

Our own recommendation is that you work at the kind of needs we have outlined above with a skilled counsellor. If this person is sympathetic to your faith, he/she will know when prayer work and/or referral to a Christian minister is appropriate.

Most Christian denominations have advisers in deliverance to whom your minister may turn. In the more traditional understanding, the casting out of evil belongs with our initiation into Christ. A review of possible occult links in order to seek a cleansing from any evil power would most helpfully occur at adult baptism or confirmation.

Deliverance prayer of this kind can be quietly authoritative and does not necessarily have to call itself 'deliverance'. It is appropriate in the context of a simple Communion service to pray for the cleansing of our family tree in order to experience a release from any 'generational' burdens.

We have answered this aspect of your question in fairly general terms which we hope might help others asking the question 'Will deliverance solve my problem?'

As we have already said, we are grateful that at Burrswood we are able to integrate prayer and counselling with medical care. You need to keep aware of all the possible lines of help (your doctor, your counsellor, your minister) without going down one route too exclusively.

## A WAY AHEAD

**Friendships, support and prayer** are vital. A praying group or a house group may provide a safe place to share and to receive. But only if it is people you can trust.

**A local self-help group** may be appropriate. Why not find out whether there is one for those with eating disorders? Advice is available on how to set one up.

You might feel embarrassed to be alongside those with anorexia and bulimia, but you will find you have much in common with their struggle. You need help and support as you resolve to journey *with* your pain rather than to anaesthetize it at regular intervals.

**Counselling help.** We have already suggested that meeting with a skilled counsellor may help you to face your suppressed pain and to open it to the healing love of Christ.

**Regular eating patterns** will help you. Try not to skip meals. Wherever possible eat in company. You may find it scary to eat regularly if you are fearful of gaining weight. But the discipline may be a key to overcoming your compulsive eating.

**Establish helplines** as a means of intervention when you feel the need to 'binge'. Two or three friends may agree that you can try ringing them. This gives you a way to look at the triggers of your eating and to talk out the misery which pushes you to eat.

**Key relationships** are crucial. Your partner or intimate friends need to know how they can help, so that they can offer encouragement as well as acceptance when you don't meet your objectives.

**Alternatives** – work out what else gives you a sense of wellbeing, e.g. physical exercise releases endorphins into the bloodstream and can give the same sense of wellbeing that a meal does. It can also reduce your appetite and it may be enjoyable in itself.

Make sure you have some *fun* in your life, social activities or hobbies. Christians can get too serious and the explicit ministry of the church does not have the answer to every need.


## CONCLUSION

Take courage. The fact that you have asked this question indicates that you are facing the reality of your struggle. The first obstacle in combating addictions is denial that they even exist. ('What, me? I haven't got a drink/food/sex problem . . .') You are already over this hurdle and we expect to see you jumping a few more in the company of good friends and the God who delights 'to set the prisoner free'.


*Helpful reading*
*Love Hunger* by Drs Minirth, Meier, Hemfelt and Sneed (Highland Books)

*Beyond Chaotic Eating* by Helena Wilkinson (HarperCollins 1993)

## Christian resource

Anorexia and Bulimia Care. **North**: 15 Fernhurst Gate, Aughton, Lancs L39 5ED. **South**: Arisaig, Back Lane, Monks Eleigh, Suffolk IP7 7BA.

# *10* When We Need Inner Healing

**Q** Please could you help me with the concept of 'inner healing'. Is it biblical? Do past areas of hurt actually catch up with us to cause pain and sickness? Would the medical profession recognize these concepts?

**A** First, we will look at whether past areas of hurt can actually catch up with us to cause pain and sickness.

It may help to offer a case history to illustrate this process, which is called somatization. By this, we mean the expressing of personal and social anguish through physical pain that is demanding of medical attention.

## INNER PAIN

### Mary

She came into the doctor's surgery with a story of recurrent right-sided stomach pain that was making her life a misery. Mary was forty-two, married to someone three years older and they had two teenage daughters. She looked well in herself but was somewhat tense and agitated.

Examination showed very evident tenderness on the right side of her stomach. The pain persisted over weeks and so she was referred to a consultant surgeon. Despite normal X-rays and scan, he decided to remove her gall bladder.

A few months later Mary was back in the surgery with similar pain. She ended up having operations to remove both her womb and appendix. Despite these, her pain persisted.

*Eventually she was either desperate enough, or felt safe enough to spill the beans, sharing the awfulness of abuse she had suffered in childhood.*

Mary was a Christian and enthusiastically took up the suggestion of receiving prayer and counselling. After several months she became pain-free; she found that the hurts of the past had become healthily integrated into her total being and overall 'wholeness'. The memories were not lost, but they were no longer disrupting life or entangling relationships in the here and now.

## AREAS OF HURT

Past areas of hurt can certainly cause ongoing physical pain. Insufficient time given to inner pain can lead to endless investigations and operations for a pain that cannot simply be excised.

Beware the motto 'When in doubt, cut it out!' Despite no identifiable organic disease, the one who is sick may hold tightly to the physical pain which is a respectable reality and demands a medical diagnosis to justify the suffering.

Gareth realized that, as a busy GP, he often needed to prescribe something because the giving of time was too costly and perhaps did not meet the expectations of the sufferer.

He wanted to earn respect by bringing about a dramatic change for the better. But sometimes we need a God-given ability to enter into solidarity with the one who suffers, acknowledging that we do not always have the answers, and that physical pain is not invalidated through the lack of a scientific explanation.

It seems that medical practice is primarily orientated towards illnesses that are well described and understood – indeed it is preoccupied with disease processes rather than looking at the processing of 'dis-ease'.

It is always important to exclude organic illnesses but it is also essential to remember that pain may represent a scream from the past and have psychosocial or spiritual roots. Plato realized this long ago, when he wrote, 'For this is the great error of our day in the treatment of the human body, that physicians separate the soul from the body.'

Despite Plato's wisdom, doctors this century have tended to apply a simplistic medical model for the diagnosis of pain. This model fails to recognize our inner humanity and the truth that, at the core of our beings, yours and ours, are fragile, hurting, bruised and alienated selves.

As hurt and alienation are accentuated through painful experiences, so lowered mood and morale have an impact on the intensity of all symptoms.

Until recent years there has been no pastoral model that would acknowledge these and point to alternative 'hidden' diagnoses.

This century has led to great advances in scientific knowledge and medical technology. There is an ever-increasing range of treatments together with extreme medical specialization that has encouraged doctors to be preoccupied with the body rather than the mind. Individual organs are investigated in isolation from the needs and experiences of the person as a whole.

Perhaps the theologian, Moltmann, has provided a way through that emphasizes the need for the medical and pastoral disciplines to work together. He wrote 'health is not a condition of my body but the power of the soul to cope with the varying conditions of that body.' This opens the door to the truth that medical resources alone cannot meet the need expressed in our inner pain. In the next case history we are trying to demonstrate the way medical and pastoral resources can work together.

## Bill

The story starts with a phone call from an angry surgical registrar at a London teaching hospital. He describes to the duty doctor at Burrswood the 'case history' of someone who has apparently wasted much medical time and money.

On his ward is a man of thirty-six years who was admitted with severe stomach pains. After two months of investigations as an in-patient he underwent a laparotomy as no definite diagnosis could be made. At operation the bowel was released in areas where it had become stuck together – adhesions, as they are called, were divided.

After surgery he had had to remain on a continuous infusion of heroin under the skin for a whole month because of persistent severe pain. The patient was then transferred to Burrswood for convalescence.

Within a day of arrival it was evident that the man was very sick. At first he was rolling around with pains that resembled having kidney stones – later he had one-sided weakness and slurred speech, symptoms that mimicked a stroke.

With the confidence that thorough investigations had been carried out, members of the care team stayed with the patient – holding him gently, sharing the pain and anguish and resisting the temptation to perform further tests.

The nurses at Burrswood realize that their authority often lies in authenticity – a modelling of how-to-be rather than how-to-do. The chaplain and counsellor were there when the patient surfaced from the confusion of past reality.

Gradually the past pain of an immense trauma earlier in his life surfaced and poured out, once the love of God had brought a feeling of safety and protection. Physical recovery followed slowly.

Having come for two weeks' convalescence, this man stayed nearly four weeks. When he had been home for a while he wrote that he had never felt so whole or so healed. He commented that being healed is so much more than just having a 'well body', although adding that that is a very good feeling too!


## PAIN AND RELEASE

We have to say that we do not often see this immediate connection that Bill experienced between the facing of inner pain and the release from physical symptoms.

Finding Christ in our pain may or may not mean that he releases us from physical agony. There is an interplay between our physical condition and our emotional/spiritual agony. Then again we may have to accept that sometimes some physical symptoms are 'needed' in order to defend someone against vulnerable inner pain.

At such times we need the recognition from the doctor and pastor alike that we are really hurting, without the implication that we are making it up or refusing to face the real issue.

There is a danger on both sides, with the pastor assuming our present debility is the consequence of our past pain and the doctor assuming that our pain must have a 'medical' explanation. The pastor may focus solely on prayer and counselling whilst the doctor may offer medication alone, perhaps allowing us to turn into 'unfeeling spectators of our own decaying selves.'

*The recognition, acceptance and provision of help for 'inner pain' is not just a matter for the doctor and pastor. It is an issue of our times.*

Many of us want to believe, above all else, that our pain has its origins in organic disease. We hesitate to admit that our suffering could be the result of spiritual or psychological factors: society still finds that unacceptable and it leaves us feeling threatened and vulnerable.

Your question encourages us because, in asking it, you are probably recognizing the effect of inner pain on your own health. It is also encouraging that many general practices offer the services of a counsellor and this is proving a popular provision.

Not all pain is eased by locating its origins in inner pain. Some find that their agony, their cry, is made in the presence of Christ, yet he doesn't cancel the pain or even ease it, but is somehow within it. Others find that he transforms the awfulness and restores the body in every way.

## INNER HEALING

We have looked at our past hurts, and how they can affect our lives, cause pain and sickness and cry out for help in differing ways. We now look at the way forward and the concept of inner healing.

*We might define 'inner healing' as giving attention to the pain of that part of our lives which lies somewhere between our sins and our physical ailments.*

The concept of inner healing was developed 20–30 years ago, associated with leading figures like Agnes Sanford, Anne White, Ruth Carter Stapleton and Francis MacNutt. It is usually connected with the need to face and to resolve hurts from the past – what has sometimes been called 'healing of memories'.

### Is it biblical?

This is rather like asking are nuclear physics or computer technology biblical? There is no explicit teaching in Scripture about a movement which is a modern convergence of psychological theories with spiritual experience.

Freud and the psycho-analytical approach have broadly influenced all of us, particularly in our understanding of the past as making us who we are in the present.

If it is true that the past still influences us, then a key biblical idea is 'Jesus Christ, the same yesterday, today, and forever' (Hebrews 13:8). Because of his timelessness, he can walk with us through the hurts of our lives and bring us freedom in the present from being controlled by the past.

Other biblical references include Psalm 139:13-16, 'For you created my inmost being . . . you knit me together in my mother's womb . . . I am fearfully and wonderfully made . . .' Here is a recognition that our present self is a living unity with our past self and that our earliest beginnings are in God.

A passage that might be used to demonstrate 'healing of memories' is John 21:15-17, where Jesus presses Simon Peter back into the pain of denying him three times, by asking him three times if he loves him. This certainly illuminates the way inner healing is often a painful exercise.

The Gospel emphasis on forgiveness (e.g. Matthew 6:14) can also be related to inner healing. Unless we keep very short accounts, the call to forgive is a call to review the past. The pain of the past is inextricably bound up with the need to forgive others who have hurt us, and there is also the need to forgive ourselves.

Then again, the laments of the Psalms can be viewed as a way to express the pain of the past in the presence of God and so to find healing. We too need to pour out our lament (Psalms 56:8; 137:1 etc).

Clearly there is not a biblical blueprint for inner healing as such, but this is not to say that the concept is unbiblical. Inner healing is rather about applying the timeless biblical gospel to the inner world of which psychological theories make us more aware. So, for example, when Jesus hung in agony on the cross he carried our innermost 'griefs and sorrows' (Isaiah 53:4) as well as our sins.

*In inner healing we allow the power of his death and resurrection to touch our internal world. The Spirit in his mission evangelizes the dark continent which is within us as well as outside us.*

## FACING OBJECTIONS

There are many objections which have been raised in relation to inner healing. Does it encourage neurotic and dependent personalities to find yet another memory that needs healing? Does it make us too introspective? Is it too individualistic when the Gospel is so much bigger than we are ourselves? Is it a luxury of a sophisticated age when we have time and money to spend on our personal wellbeing?

All of these questions need to be heard. A biblical objection may be found in the concept of 'new creation in Christ' (2 Corinthians 5:17). If 'the old has gone' and 'the new has come' what are we doing raking over the embers of the past? But the truth that we are a new creation in Christ does not of itself enable us to experience a simple transition from old to new.

The Spirit's work of recreating us is more messy than we often like to think. And our past needs baptizing into Christ. We have known Christians who have used the 'new creation' theory to suppress past pain, until that pain has pushed through into their consciousness and demanded to be heard. This sometimes happens via physical symptoms as your question implies and as we have tried to address above.

## HOW IT HAPPENS

The ideal is that we are able naturally to process the past in the presence of God, opening its sins and sorrows to the cleansing love of Christ. The regular practice of gathering up and 're-collecting' our experience, both the positives and the negatives, is fundamental to our health. It is one of the benefits of daily prayer, for example, as we review the day prayerfully before going to sleep.

It may be that our neglect of this leads to the build-up of unprocessed hurts and resentments. As we review the day or the week, can we hear what our feelings are saying? What is the message of our blackness, our tiredness, our backache?

We can do a good deal of inner healing work on our own, for example by making a list from time to time of people we may need to forgive, of hurts received by us, and of hurts inflicted by us. We may open these to the power and refining of the Spirit by burning them, maybe with someone else to support us and pray with us.

The concept of inner healing does not necessarily require someone else to minister to us. A self-help book (see below) may enable us to open our past to the movement of the Holy Spirit. Prayer ministries of different kinds often address this area.

It is important to grasp that there is no easy way of receiving inner healing. The deep work of the Holy Spirit may enable us to be more truly aware of, and bear, our innermost pain.

If you are involved in ministering to others, please remember that memories cannot be simply erased by claiming the presence of Jesus in them. Some techniques have seemed to suggest that this is possible.

It is a fallacy to imply that the Lord can somehow change the past. What *can* change is our *attitude* to the past so that we find grace to live with it. But for most of us this is a long and difficult process.

Prayer ministries may need the complementary work of skilled and experienced counsellors. For example, painful memories may surface when we are prayed for in the power of the Spirit, but may often need the healing process of a much more careful and skilled professional counselling relationship.

## WHAT CAN HAPPEN?

Someone called David illustrates his experience in a poem. He put into words what was happening in his life, thanks to the help of his family, his church and ministry at Burrswood.

Sometimes, part of me hurts
I'm not completely sure why
A part of me
I find hard to accept
Aches
And wants to express itself
In a way I don't really like

Long ago
Someone damaged me
Exposed a weakness
I didn't know was there.
And for years I hid the pain
Until
Suddenly
One day
Life brought it back up again.

And all the anger
The hurt
The pain

I suppose deep inside
I feel rejected.
I can't accept
That this can be
Really me.
And I try and try
To hide the hurt,
The feelings
I can no longer
Own as mine.

But you can't disguise
The part of you
That you hate to see.
And like a sleeping
Volcano
Sometimes I erupt
You see.
I can no longer
Hide the pain
For God in his love

*Will spew out*
*And spill over*
*White hot*

*Enraged,*
*So long repressed*
*And simmering inside.*

*But there is a love*
*Which is slowly melting me*
*A peace deep inside*
*Which is helping me*
*To understand*
*How God really first made*
*Me in his Great Design.*
*And slowly*
*Like Beauty and the Beast*
*I can learn to accept*
*That part of me*
*Which is crying out for love.*

*My ugliness can be changed*
*Can be moulded*
*Into something beautiful*
*And worthwhile again.*

*Is giving me courage*
*To face what I hate*

*And love breaks through*
*And love heals.*
*And love restores*
*As I see Jesus*
*Suffered and died for me.*
*He broke the chains*
*Which tie me down*
*He took the sting*
*Out of all the lies*
*Which Satan would fling.*

*And a lie when exposed*
*To the light*
*Loses its power to afflict*
*To tear you inside out.*

*Thank you Jesus*
*That through you*
*I can love myself*
*Accept myself*
*And slowly grow*
*Into the person*
*You really want me to be.*

## CONCLUSION

We cannot brush aside the complexities which your question raises. What we can do is to register the importance of inner pain. As we do this we are more than ever convinced of the need for the medical and pastoral worlds to work in partnership so that 'inner healing' can become more of a reality.

### *Helpful reading*
*Healing the Hidden Self* by Barbara Schlemon (Ave Maria Press).

*Listening to your Feelings* by Myra Chave-Jones (Lion).

# *11* The Importance of Touch

**Q I am a member of a church pastoral team. After much discussion, we remain unclear as to the importance and appropriateness of 'touch' in the ministry of healing. I would value your insights.**

**A** Thank you for asking about this important aspect of ministry. It was Desmond Morris who commented that we often talk about the way we talk, and we frequently try to see the way we see, but for some reason we rarely touch on the way we touch!

We know only too well how mistakes can happen so easily when this whole issue is not carefully worked through – and the mistakes will be anything but healing for those involved.

It has been said that 'to touch is not a technique; not touching is a technique'. We develop this further below.

## For life

It was Aristotle who argued that physical touch is the most fundamental of all the five senses.

This is never more so than at both ends of life. It is significant that touch is the earliest sense to develop and provide us with a fundamental means of interacting with our environment and with others.

Touch is of overwhelming importance to us from the moment of birth in providing security and a healthy nurturing. We see many people who are emotionally sick because patterns of attachment have been broken through inappropriate or absent touch early in life.

As infants we are quick to learn that caring touch and cuddling provide reassurance, comfort and relief from the anxieties that accompany separation.

In times of sickness, isolation may be a reality and this allows feelings from any similar earlier experience to surface.

Touch brings a sense of security: it reassures us that someone is with us in our distress, that we are not alone. This nurturing touch brings a sense of being valued and accepted; it expresses concern and compassion and often facilitates a sharing of emotional feelings, a release of pent-up emotion.

Later in life, personal loss – loss of health, loss of loved ones and particularly loss of acute sensation in the limbs – increases the need for touch. Perhaps most of us need a regular dose of appropriate body contact to remain healthy!

We all vary in the amount of touch we give and are happy to receive from others. During times of stress, when health and security are threatened, touch may become especially therapeutic and restorative; it becomes a vital prescription for health and healing.

At the same time we need to be aware that touch can bring the wrong message. It does not always communicate love and care; formalized purposeful touch can be cold and clinical. Sometimes, repressed violent, hostile or sexual feelings can unknowingly be off-loaded by the carer in this way.

## Practical caring

Most of those in the caring professions have not been taught the value of clinical touch at any time during their training.

As a doctor at Burrswood, Gareth has had to learn that it is not always appropriate to take the patient by the hand or to sit on the bed when listening. He now asks permission or draws up a chair to an appropriate place.

We all have a 'comfort bubble' around us into which others are unwelcome. The size of this bubble varies according to our present vulnerability, and our experience of touch, particularly in the early years.

Practical caring entails the deliberate physical contact associated with nursing procedures such as washing or lifting the one who is sick. It also allows for expressive, spontaneous touch that is unrelated to a particular task.

Touch is used so often in practical caring that we may use it without realizing how healing and therapeutic it can be.

Sometimes carers find their hands seem empty, when there is no longer anything to be done. It is particularly then that we need to look to our hands as a channel of God's love and healing.

At this uncomfortable time, for we tend to feel more comfortable 'doing' rather than 'being', touch communicates and comforts often far more than words and actions can. Physical touch connects us with our humanness and prevents us feeling 'out of touch' with others.

Even with practical caring, touch needs to be used carefully. We need to be aware of our own responses to touching the sick in different ways.

Even when the boundaries are well defined, as in nursing, routine touch can be interpreted as hurtful or provocative, depending on past experience. The message conveyed cannot easily be changed or corrected.

## Therapeutic touch and comfort

Touch is not experienced solely as physical sensation – it is also experienced as an emotion. In this way, touch can bring healing to body, mind and spirit.

Many find their physical pain eased when the pain is shared, their hand is held. The muscle tension from fear, anxiety and physical strain is eased by systematic purposeful touch in the form of massage. Gentle strokes can induce relaxation of the whole being.

This secure, accepting environment may allow inner pains of the past to surface, it may open the door to deep inner healing.

At Burrswood, we have to think carefully whether this is appropriate as the timing of such a release is so important. Massage on the day of discharge could allow inner pain to surface when there is no one literally to hold the situation and be alongside in love and prayer.

Massage is often helpful alongside more invasive and specifically therapeutic treatments. Indeed, in a study of patients receiving radiotherapy for breast cancer, those undergoing back massage reported significantly less physical distress, tiredness and tension.

As long as the sick remain strangers, caring can hardly be meaningful.

Therapeutic touch can be a way of breaking down barriers and establishing relationships.

### In the Bible

In the Old Testament, hands were laid on as a sign of the passing on of God's blessing. In the Gospels, touch is referred to many times as an important part of the way Jesus dealt with people. Norman Autton comments, 'God sent his Son in order that we may touch God and that God may touch us.'

The New Testament makes the claim that 'our hands have touched . . . that which was from the beginning' (1 John 1:1).

Jesus then both touched and allowed himself to be touched. In touching him others were healed (Luke 8:44). He engaged in physical contact beyond expected norms, as with the woman who kissed his feet while washing them with her tears and drying them with her hair (Luke 7:38).

Holding the man with leprosy expressed acceptance and solidarity (Mark 1:41). Babies were brought to him explicitly to be touched (Luke 18:15). He often used touch to convey healing, but this was clearly not essential since he could 'say the word' and it was effective (Luke 7:7).

The early church continued to use hands to express the healing power of the Holy Spirit (e.g. Acts 9:12). As followers of Jesus we will want to be those who, like him, are able to touch and be touched. We will want to continue the ministry of his 'living touch' (Dorothy Kerin).

### Guidelines for a pastoral team

We are impressed that as a team you are already talking about this. It is good that you take time to reflect together and to ask important questions.

Touching, we repeat, is not a technique and we cannot tell you *how* to do it. The way we touch others flows from who we are and therefore needs to be a genuine expression of warmth, acceptance and support. So be natural and be yourself.

## Our reactions

We cannot easily touch or be touched in a dispassionate way. If we did it would be a denial of our humanity.

Members of a pastoral team need a high level of self-awareness. Holding the hand of a dying person may be our saying a fearful 'don't leave me' rather than 'I am with you.'

More commonly, such helpers sometimes use caring relationships as a substitute for really touching the people close to them.

We may have to ask ourselves ruthless questions, e.g. 'Is touching in my caring work more intimate than in my marriage and family life?' Strong emotional reactions in us when we seek to care for others are not wrong. They are to be expected. But they do need monitoring.

In a relationship where we are really 'with' somebody else, our own feelings are engaged as we tune into their need. The stages we can learn here are:

1  register what we are feeling: e.g. we may feel like holding a person gently and tenderly, like a mother holding a baby;
2  decide how to respond: in this example, we might do any number of things such as
   — use our feelings in order to pray quietly as the encounter continues, picturing God holding the person;
   — use it as a cue, perhaps to show the person a picture of outstretched hands and see how they react;
   — offer a Scripture like Isaiah 49:14–16;
   — actually offer a level of touch if this seems right;
3  debrief afterwards with a support person.

## Supervision

You can see from this example how crucial it is to have someone to come back to in order to check things out, both for yourself and the person you are helping.

This is particularly true if you are doing one-to-one work where what has been called a 'gruesome twosome' can develop – often a collusion between someone who is needy and someone else who 'needs to care'. Such snarl-ups require the objectivity of a third person in order to disentangle them.

A key question to ask ourselves is, 'Are there aspects of my pastoral work with someone, including the use of touch, that I am not able to talk about with a confidential support person?' If so, this is a real danger signal – get yourself some help!

## Caution and safety

We would recommend that you are cautious in your use of touch in private one-to-one encounters unless you are really well trained and supervised.

Even if you think it is 'all right' or 'in the Spirit', the person you are touching is likely to be experiencing strong responses. You may wake up one day with the realization that you have become emotionally over-involved, decide to withdraw, and leave them helplessly damaged by your insensitivity.

Pastoral touch can be made safer by the location, e.g. prayer ministry using a degree of touch feels safer in scattered twos and threes in a quiet corner of the church than in a private room.

Church pastoral teams sometimes choose to work in twos, which gives greater safety and is more effective with a man and a woman working together.

We have heard of pastoral teams where team members only help people of the same sex as themselves. This is understandable and possibly advisable in low-key pastoral encounters. However, the God-given dynamic between men and women is something we need not be afraid to use, provided there is skilled supervision to hand.

## A time not to

You may want to reflect in your team on when it is inappropriate to use touch. 'There is a time for everything . . . a time to embrace and a time to refrain' (Ecclesiastes 3:5).

When engaged in listening work it is common to sit a little way apart from someone: holding them at this stage fails to keep the necessary 'therapeutic space'.

Many trained counsellors deliberately abstain from touch. When someone bursts into tears, is it your need or theirs that causes you to put an arm around them?

Touching too soon can inhibit the release of sorrow and may 'tell' the person that you cannot bear the full force of their feelings.

Some form of supportive touch often seems natural as we pray with another person. But some people are deeply afraid of the intimacy that even this level of touch implies.

Sometimes, but not always, you will pick up this feeling and know intuitively that you are not to touch unless clear permission is given. Those who have been physically abused require this kind of sensitivity.

If in doubt, don't! Abuse can be repeated by would-be helpers. But you may learn to ask in a natural way, 'I am wondering if I can put a hand here on your back while I pray?'

## What can happen?

It is easy to think that you would use different guidelines when working with those who have suffered abuse in some way, yet you will rarely know much of a person's intimate and painful past. Just as in nursing and medical care, it is best to use routinely clinical procedures that would prevent transmission of the HIV virus, so in pastoral care it is safer to remember the possibility of past abuse and to care accordingly. When alongside those who have been sexually abused, it is vital to realize that when areas of this kind are entrusted to you, there is a highly charged situation. Having made disclosures, the one you are caring for will feel vulnerable and powerless and these feelings will echo the circumstances of their abuse. In this relationship any form of touch is open to misunderstandings. If the one seeking help is a woman and her key worker from your team is a man, a familiarity and trust can develop that allows sensible boundaries to be eroded. The pastoral carer may find himself experiencing a closeness and fulfilment that is inappropriate and the person who has been abused may find that the comfort she receives leads on to affection. Touch now has a new meaning and interpretation that was not originally intended.

## A spectrum

You may find it helpful to distinguish between the poles of what we would call 'supportive' and 'intimate' touch. 'Supportive' touch can be regarded as firm and fairly static – a hand on the shoulder or a pat on the back. 'Intimate' touch is lighter and may tend to probe as in sexual touching.

Clearly this is a spectrum with 'friendship' or 'companionship' touch somewhere in between. A lot of what is felt to be acceptable is culturally conditioned, e.g. kissing. What is important is to know where you are on the spectrum. And professional 'therapeutic' touch can be very intimate as in nursing attention, massage or osteopathy.

If you are engaging in intimate touch in pastoral situations, this may be appropriate (as with Jesus and the woman in Luke 7) but it needs to be understood as professional by all concerned. And it requires clear accountability and close supervision.

## Touch of authority

There is a laying-on of hands which is a formal expression of God's blessing and healing. Some Christian healing approaches encourage laying hands on the diseased part of a person's body. We would not ourselves go this way since we understand that the whole person is involved in a healing process.

We have some caution about the concept of direct healing energies flowing from our hands. Interestingly, the laying-on of hands usually involves touching the head, which in everyday relating is a highly intimate action. As such it needs safeguarding.

The laying-on of hands is a tangible way of passing on the power and authority of Christ and his church, and care should be taken to ensure that those who offer this formal ministry are duly authorized.

It is only such a careful balance of intimacy and authority which can safely cherish what is one of the loveliest gifts within the life of God's church. This is nothing less than enacting the touch of Christ himself.


# CONCLUSION

Yes, it is right to express cautions and to keep our pastoral practice safe. But there is also a godly risk in daring to reach out and touch one another in his love. Touch is vital to our life, to our healing, and to our fellowship in Christ. We believe in touch!

Among the l'Arche Communities founded by Jean Vanier, the universal language of touch brings together able-bodied helpers and the handicapped alike. One of their hymns translated from the French, 'Les Mains de Dieu', leaves us to respond to the question:

The hands of God have been laid upon our sorrowful faces, the hands of God have caressed our wounded hearts giving relief, at last, from the flames of our suffering. Will our hands be laid in this way too?


*Helpful reading*
*The Laying on of Hands* by Carolyn Headley (Grove Booklet, Worship Series 104)
*Touch: An Exploration* by Norman Autton (Darton, Longman & Todd)
*Hidden Treasure* by Green and Townsend (Darton, Longman & Todd)

## *12* Dealing with Anger

**Q** I find I am an angry Christian and my anger spills out unpredictably. I find it hard to allow myself to be angry. My sense of guilt gets in the way. I also find it hard to forgive people who made my life awful years ago. I think this is making me ill. I am always unwell and my doctor cannot find a reason for this.

**A** Thank you for your question. We find it so encouraging that you are able to recognize your anger and relate it to your lack of well-being. We all have anger but often find that hard to acknowledge. We wonder whether you have looked at the place of anger in the Scriptures?

### ANGER IN THE BIBLE

There is every indication in Scripture that God himself experiences great anger.

Isaiah 13 speaks of 'the wrath of the Lord Almighty' expressed on 'the day of his burning anger'. God's anger burns in the cause of all that is right and against all that opposes it.

Sometimes in the heart of God there seems to be a struggle between his fierce anger and his intense love for his people, e.g. 'How can I give you up, Ephraim? How can I hand you over, Israel? . . . My heart is changed within me; all my compassion is aroused. I will not carry out my fierce anger . . . for I am God, and not man – the Holy One among you. I will not come in wrath' (Hosea 11:8-9).

Jesus of course was totally at home with his anger. He used quite strong words to spell out what he thought about the hypocrisy of religious leaders – described variously as 'foxes', 'sons of vipers', 'children of the devil', 'ravening wolves', 'whited sepulchres'. Intense anger at the plight of the human condition seemed closely linked to his acts of compassion.

Mark makes this connection as Jesus was being challenged by legalistic attitudes to his healing on the Sabbath: 'He looked round at them in anger and sorrow' . . . (Mark 3:5).

The 'cleansing' of the temple is often cited as an example of Jesus definitely *not* 'meek and mild'. There in the temple he gave a display of anger which was a genuine venting of fury, when compared to the controlled if convincing performance of a skilful classroom teacher.

He was not only showing expertly that he was angry; he was giving expression to that anger. According to John's account (John 2:13-17), he made a whip and used it – this was a highly physical encounter.

## POURED OUT IN PSALMS

But what about *our* anger? We in the main find it excruciatingly difficult to hold our 'wrath' and our 'compassion' in balance. Not many of us could risk a cleansing of the temple without fearing that we would totally lose our rag!

The Psalms give us a methodology whereby we can vent our unrefined anger in the presence of God. Everything gets poured out. It may be written down, sung or shouted. It may contain quite outrageous sentiments.

A stark example here is that desire for vengeance in Psalm 137: 'O Daughter of Babylon . . . happy is he who repays you for what you have done to us – he who seizes your infants and dashes them against the rocks' (Psalms 137:8-9).

*One of the messages of the Psalms is that God wants to hear, and the people of God may offer to him, all the muddle of our feelings including our anger.*

There is a safety in expressing them in this way, and it is only after doing so that we may be able to sift what is holy wrath from what is sinful vindictiveness.

The expressing of all their strong feelings by the psalmists is a form of 'catharsis'. Similarly we often need some way to release our strong feelings in a safe context before we can use our anger constructively in our daily living and relating.

Offering our own psalm to God is one such way. We may indeed be able to write it as a letter, 'Dear God . . . this is what I feel.' We may then burn it, or take it to a trusted friend who, with or without reading it in our presence, may stand with us as we burn it. Our experience at Burrswood suggests that people take and use this symbolism in the way that is meaningful to them.

Our burning anger may appear to be taken up into the flames of God's wrath. A common idea that seems helpful is of the flames as the 'refining' of the Spirit.

Some at least of our vengeful rantings, consumed in the heat of the Spirit's fire, emerge as holy wrath. Then again, to place our letter under a cross or crucifix in a safe setting (such as one of the chapels at Burrswood) helps us direct the strength of our anger to a God-given place.

*We need somewhere to take our fury. Jesus himself at the cross bears the vindictive fury of all time; and so we may begin to feel that ours is heard and redeemed.*

In the process we call forgiveness, it is only when we have got to the point of releasing the depth of our hurt, often expressed in anger, that we are then able to begin to forgive from the heart.

## 'BE ANGRY BUT SIN NOT'

In this famous verse (Ephesians 4:26), Paul encourages us not to go to bed with our anger still raging.

In attempting to follow his instruction too literally, Christians have often denied or repressed their anger. 'Christians shouldn't be angry', we say. This is not so. Because we are human, and because anger is part of God himself, we will feel angry every day of our lives.

What Paul says here seems to commend the practice of reviewing the day before we go to sleep. After an angry outburst, instead of just sticking to our guns, we need calmly to sift what may have been wrong or unhelpful in the way our anger was expressed.

It is perhaps the *nursing* of anger which is sinful, and anger when it is nursed thrives only too well!

Ruthless honesty with ourselves is required to face how much we are secretly or openly nursing anger and resentments.

With major conflicts, it is quite unrealistic to expect to settle them before the sun sets. What is important is not that we resolve everything immediately, but that we are open to a process both of self-examination and of constructive communication, when we can, with other people involved in the conflict.

There are no easy answers, as whole countries torn apart by violence and war demonstrate. But as Christians we are people of hope believing that anger does not have to be destructive in God's final purposes. First, we need to realize that anger is in all of us and has to be handled from our earliest days.

## ANGER FROM BIRTH

Very early in life we discover that anger is an emotion that arises from the deepest part of our being. It is so strong that it cannot easily be pushed aside.

The scream at birth may be our first experience of anger. Imagine how we might feel at being pushed precariously away from our comfortable environment that was centrally heated, with food on tap and the reassuring heartbeat of maternal love, into one that involves struggle and effort on our part; an environment with dazzling lights and, in days gone by, the initiation ceremony of a spank on the bottom!

In childhood we experience inconsistent patterns of control, unreasonable expectations, excessive strictness, over-protectiveness and over-indulgence perhaps.

Even at eighteen months, we find a strong need for autonomy and independence. And yet our lack of experience and our inability verbally to express our needs holds us back.

We find that our longings and drives are out of balance with our competence and our ability to cope. We scream in frustration and anger. If we are bored, hungry, tired or ill, our tolerance for frustration is less, and anger wells up and spills over.

This is all similar to feelings generated in similar situations in adulthood. But, by then, we have worked out coping strategies, based in experience and our developed abilities. So a degree of tolerance is found.

Some of us, from an early age, are more naturally placid, positive and adaptable, while others of us are more active and determined, and have more difficulty accepting limits and coping with disappointment. In the latter situations an outburst of anger is a more common occurrence.

You mention that you find it hard to allow yourself to be angry. This is not surprising since as children we quickly learn that anger is unacceptable to adults. We have to suppress it because they cannot cope with it and this learning sets a pattern that is often carried over into adulthood.

## THE PROCESSING OF ANGER

How anger affects our bodies has been understood from very early in history.

In the works of Lactantius we read: 'The eyes gleam, the countenance trembles, the tongue stammers, the teeth chatter, the visage is alternately stained now with redness spread over it, now with white paleness.'

The next time you are angry, make a note (if you can divert your thoughts) of all the physical reactions going on in your body. The tightness of the chest, the cramping stomach, the palpitations thudding in your ears, the sweating palms and the enlarged pupils. All show that your body is preparing for crisis.

Adrenalin and other chemicals are racing around your bloodstream; these increase your heart rate, blood pressure and rate of breathing, and make glucose available to energize your tensed muscles. Your stomach ceases digestion as blood is diverted to your brain and your skin.

It is not surprising that all this can affect health, especially if anger rumbles on deep within. It may only express itself in physical 'disease', the cause of which confuses the medical practitioners.

At this stage, anger is still an internal process whereby the feelings of annoyance, irritation and arousal are being experienced through these symptoms. These persist on and off until anger is released, often through an uncontrolled outburst, cynicism or other angry behaviour.

You can see why anger is defined as an 'emotional state that consists of feelings of irritation, annoyance, fury or rage with heightened arousal of the "fight or flight" defence reaction' (that prepares one for fighting or fleeing from perceived danger).

## ANGER AND ILLNESS

If not recognized, anger may emerge in a variety of disguises such as disabling illness, inappropriate behaviour and chronic unhappiness.

Anger may not only be a critical response to illness but also an exacerbating agent, triggering or advancing it.

Anger has repeatedly been shown to be linked with an increasing risk of disease in the heart and arteries, and heart attacks, strokes and high blood pressure.

Anger is an inflammatory state, and so it is not surprising that it has been associated with inflammation of the joints (arthritis), the guts (gastritis and colitis) and 'angry rashes' (dermatitis). Needless to say, having one of these conditions does not mean that it must have been triggered by anger. It is often difficult to know which comes first.

In rheumatoid arthritis, for example, the losses of ability, potential and interpersonal relationships are themselves stressful and may result in a spiral of anger as each new loss is recognized.

If left as 'anger within', this may aggravate joint inflammation creating further loss. Such a process is difficult to prove scientifically as unexpressed emotion is hard to quantify.

Anger can disrupt our emotional as well as our physical health. Anger within may well cause depression. In particular, depressive reactions to crisis like divorce, bereavement, illness and impending death have been linked to anger seeking expression.

Research suggests that when anger is a major component of depression, we are more likely to punish ourselves and even attempt suicide. Likewise physical assault can be an unhealthy expression of rage in someone whose anger has turned to depression.

Doctors working with patients who suffer from chronic pain of no identifiable cause have noted significant childhood trauma in over 90 per cent of cases.

*Early trauma brings a feeling of helplessness, children being unable to make sense of what has happened to them. In turn, the helplessness engenders anger which becomes destructive to health.*

This anger may come out as a desire to victimize others in one way or another. Its expression may, on the other hand, become inhibited as in those who have suffered sexual abuse. Here inappropriate shame and guilt stir up deep anger and aggression.

Unresolved anger may lead to chronic pain.

All in all, it is not surprising that you relate your anger to illness. Anger held within, whether identified or not, is very draining of energy. Muscles held in tension, heart beating fast, stomach churning – all this saps energy and makes everyday living a struggle.

At Burrswood, we have found that there is often unexpressed anger in those suffering from ME and similar illnesses.

Whether anger has dampened the immune system, allowing a virus to take hold, or whether anger is the result of chronic weakness and frustration, it is difficult to say.

There is little doubt that such chronic illness lowers self-esteem and that one of the major triggers for anger is a threat to our self-esteem. Hence there is the potential for a spiral down into poor emotional and physical health.

## GETTING HELP

You talk about your anger spilling out unpredictably. We hope that you can now see why this happens.

You may have found that one result is that there are fewer friends around you. Anger in us brings out anger in them and they can begin to offer quietly negative 'friendship' with hostility hidden behind their smiling faces.

You may be feeling defenceless and abandoned. If so, it is now that you will discover that anger is not all bad and that its energy can be harnessed for good.

William Blake wrote:

I was angry with my friend;
I told my wrath, my wrath did end.
I was angry with my foe:
I told it not, my wrath did grow.

How do you stop it growing? Well, we have already described the use of creative writing, designing our own psalm in order to be in touch with and release some of our strong feelings.

We all find our own mechanisms for safely expelling the enormous build-up of energy which anger creates within us. Some*one* to talk to and some*thing* to thump are indispensable allies.

We all need someone who can understand and bear the strength of negativity which comes from our angry reactions. Our marriage partners and close companions can sometimes help us by listening to the full force of our rage. But it is probably advisable to have somebody else a little more detached with whom we can 'offload'.

Something to thump can really help when we are at our most frustrated. David keeps a sponge 'mallet' (given by a friend) on his desk – this also preserves a sense of humour about it all.

Smiling at ourselves is important because our real need is to make friends with our anger and not to be frightened by it. We may find other mechanisms which help, like screaming while driving the car (alone – and keep your eyes on the road!), or shouting in a safe place, or flinging a stone into a pond. Gareth goes into the garden and clears the undergrowth with unusual energy.

We might also learn to 'take care of the angry child within'. David was struggling to cope with his anger at difficult meetings. A counsellor suggested that he should 'put' his angry 'child' in his pocket before the meeting. When things became difficult he could pat his pocket gently and say 'You're all right, I've got you!' This helps him, because his fear and his anger are closely related. Simple as they are, such concepts can benefit us as we use them prayerfully.


## A WORD OF CAUTION

The ways that we have described above will not help you if you are really frightened of the immense volcano of anger within you. Your question seems to suggest that, as you start to release your anger in some of these ways, you may begin to realize how powerful and dangerous it is 'down there'.

At these moments it is probably best to stop, and pray: ask the Lord to 'hold' the strength of your anger safe in his care. Or a relatively small event may trigger enormous waves of violent fury which will 'spill out' as you put it. 'I don't know what came over me', you say.

If you are deeply afraid of your anger, and also feel guilty about it and are unable to say 'hello' to it with a smile, we suggest that you seek some help from a trusted, confidential person.

You are already aware of the people you find it hard to forgive. Looking at this carefully with someone skilful whom you trust may help you. You *will* find it impossible to forgive them in any deep sense until you have been helped to direct and release your anger with them.

## CONSTRUCTIVE ANGER

Above all, we need to make friends with this energy, which is our anger, so that it can be put to constructive use for God's kingdom. It has so many rich possibilities.

Myra Chave-Jones writes: 'There are probably only two emotions . . . which hold within them such tremendous potential. They are love and anger.'

For example, we can harness our anger and use it as prayer; we can make it the energy with which we work; we can put it into hard physical exercise.

Anger gives energy to protest and so can help to bring about change. It has been said that it is the anger in compassion that makes it a force for change. So, most powerfully, like Christ, we can link our anger to our compassion. Put this immense God-given energy behind a really good cause.

Don't waste your anger on a *person*. Rather, be angry about something worth being passionate about. And *do* something to put it right!

We might then begin to glimpse the possibility that our anger, properly harnessed and directed, can, like God's wrath (Isaiah 13:13), shake the world more into the shape he wants it to be.

### Helpful reading
*Living with Anger* by Myra Chave-Jones (Triangle, SPCK)
*The Gospel of Anger* by Alastair V Campbell (SPCK)

# *13* Understanding the Journey of Grief

**Q** I am helping someone whose husband died just a year ago. She cared for him for twenty months and was in some ways relieved when he died. Now she feels ill and is unable to concentrate, yet our friends in the church think she should be back to normal. She thinks she is going mad. Your advice please.

**A** Thank you for your question. We feel it is highly important that Christian people get a basic understanding of the grieving process.

Grief is a natural and God-given journey whereby we come to terms with traumatic loss. It is not therefore something that Christians can bypass as if their faith somehow gives them immunity from what is in reality the cost of loving.

One of the most important, and shortest, verses in Scripture is John 11:35: 'Jesus wept.' He wept at the grave of his friend, and he was no stranger to 'loud cries and tears' (Hebrews 5:7).

Often it is our experience that the most helpful thing we can do for a grieving person is to reassure him/her that the often frightening symptoms they are experiencing are precisely to do with their grief.

This applies, for example, to your comments about your friend feeling ill, being unable to concentrate, and wondering if she is going mad.

*It is certainly advantageous to know something of the terrain for people in grief, to have a 'map' for the journey.*

The 'stages of grief' have often been identified and labelled in different ways. Because it is a highly disorientating and confusing experience, a map can give us some clues as to where we have

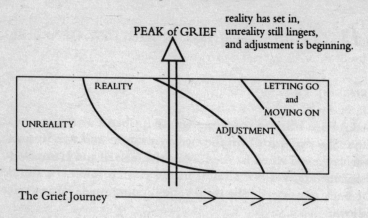

The Grief Journey

reached as well as to assure us that we are 'on the map'.

In a way grief is indeed a kind of madness and we need help to know that this is a path that others have trodden. One such person is C. S. Lewis, who described the feelings of losing his wife in *A Grief Observed* – portrayed in the film *Shadowlands*. Just the introduction might help your friend:

> No one ever told me that grief felt so like fear. I am not afraid, but the sensation is like being afraid. The same fluttering in the stomach, the same restlessness, the yawning. I keep on swallowing. At other times it feels like being mildly drunk, or concussed . . .

For the sake of simplicity we might view the grief process as a four-fold one, though we do not move from one stage to another at clearly defined points. Rather, the stages give way to each other very subtly, and at times the force of a stage we thought we had come through returns with unexpected poignancy.

As the diagram suggests, at the 'peak' of grief no one stage is completely resolved and we are in a melting pot of confusion.

In terms of the passage of time, as a rough guide we might observe that grief peaks at about six months to a year after the loss. (Grieving for a dying relative, as with your friend's husband, obviously begins well before the moment of death.)

The whole process will certainly not be reaching the final stages until one to two years have passed – considerably longer in the case of losing marriage partners, parents or children.

### Unreality: 'I don't believe it'
The first stage of grief is a shock reaction and we cannot absorb painful truth in one go.

In that early phase we experience a numbness which protects us from being overwhelmed and there may be a euphoria which carries us through.

Relief is a very common reaction; we are genuinely pleased that our loved ones have gone to a better place, glad that their suffering is over, as well as being released ourselves from the burden of caring for them.

The unreality theme of 'somehow I still can't believe it' recurs throughout the grief process. We hope we will wake up from the dream. Or we imagine the dead person as gone on a long holiday from which they will soon return.

### Reality: 'I can't bear it'
The natural anaesthetic of stage one wears off as we gradually absorb the pain of our loss, and the reality of the loved one's absence becomes more and more acute.

We may feel anxious about not being able to cope alone and often become aware of our own mortality.

Almost certainly this is the point your friend has reached. The early relief that her husband's illness was over, has swung as she faces the enormity of her loss and her loneliness.

If the relationship with the deceased person was a troubled one, the pain can be more acute than we might expect. We are *not* glad to see the back of them; rather we are prone to regrets about what might have been and guilts about our seeming failures and omissions. Our feelings of guilt are often inappropriate – later to be eased by the return of undistorted reality.

Stage two is when we express ourselves in endless weeping from deep inside. We cry and cry but we do not exhaust the grief: it seems to exhaust us, leaving us apathetic and listless.

Grieving is hard work, and this needs recognizing by others. All kinds of physical, mental, and spiritual symptoms can occur (including the ones you mention) and we may be unable to cope with the smallest of everyday demands.

## Physical symptoms

C. S. Lewis described well the physical symptoms that we commonly experience. We may also find a tightness in the chest or throat, a dry mouth and extreme muscle weakness. All this contributes to a sense of unreality, and a fear of serious illness.

If these symptoms persist in your friend and become more troublesome, do suggest that a talk with her family doctor is a good idea. We think it would be wise for her to explore with her doctor, and if appropriate with a counsellor, what the feeling 'ill' is about.

Sometimes in grief we develop symptoms of the loved one's illness and even believe we ourselves are seriously ill in the way they were. Is this what the 'madness' is, we wonder?

On the other hand, we may be so taken up with caring for our loved one that we give no thought to our own health.

In these times we can either miss the fact that something is not right or feel that it is too minor to worry about when compared to the advancing disease in the one we love. Our health is vulnerable at this time as is shown by the fact that many an elderly person dies literally of a 'broken heart' within months of the death of their partner.

Grief also disturbs our immune response system leaving us more exposed to infections, arthritis and even secondary cancer. So you can see that when we are grieving it is important to try and look after our health. It is tempting to fill up on coffee, tea and snack foods rather than bothering to eat a balanced meal.

We will benefit from trying to take a little exercise even if it is the last thing we feel like. We may fear meeting people we know when we go out and anyway feel too weak to make the effort, but it will help. Gentle exercise may help us to sleep better and to relax generally.

Very gradually our immune system recovers again as we find our way through the worst of our inner pain and bewilderment.

At this stage in grief, other symptoms, besides the lack of concentration that your friend has noticed, may include an inability to order our mind.

We can also find that we are preoccupied with thoughts about our loved one and often have a sense of their presence, especially in the month or two after their death. We may even have experiences when we think we have seen or heard our beloved. All this is a usual part of grieving.

At this stage, we often find the little sleep we do get is punctuated by dreams about the one who has died. We may struggle to eat, lose weight and find we have no interest in the outside world. When we do get out and about we may find ourselves revisiting places that have important memories as well as treasuring physical reminders of our loved one.

With all this going on, it is not surprising that this second stage is the overwhelming phase of grief when we seem totally unable to handle anything. Our feelings may well get put onto other things or people.

Anger is poured out at doctors, ministers, God himself. Anger may be triggered by feelings of frustration and helplessness in that nothing could prevent death.

We may appear to our helpers to be totally selfish: the truth is that we are, and we *need* to be, self-absorbed at this point in the process.

This is often the stage at which would-be helpers express frustrations or give up, and being alongside a grieving person in the peak of their pain is hard work in itself.

### Adjustment: 'What can I do to handle it?'
Because the depth of our pain has been reached we begin to find some energy to work at how to move forward. So in stage three we

start to face what life is like without our loved one.

The turning points of anniversaries, and your friend is at the first one, can be painful but productive. So can times like birthdays or Christmas and first visits to places or social contexts which we associate with the person we have lost.

Adjustment also includes coming to terms with changes in social status like becoming a 'widow' – undoubtedly this will be poignant for your friend.

In trying to tie up unfinished business of our relationship we must beware of being drawn into visiting mediums or in any way trying to contact the one who has died.

In some way we need to release the person who has died into Jesus' loving arms and then love Jesus and those left behind with that same love that could otherwise be stifled in loneliness.

That sounds straightforward but often is only partially achieved this side of heaven. The book *Requiem Healing* (see book list) may help you in this area.

### Letting go and moving on: 'I feel better but I'll never be the same again'

In the final stage of grieving we begin to live again. Something within us, a whole part of us, has died with the loved one: and something also comes to new life as we chart our course without them.

We find emotional energy to invest in new interests and we also begin to risk loving again. But we are never the same and adjusting to loss is certainly not returning to 'normal'.

*The expectation of your church friends is therefore unrealistic and unhelpful. Because grief is a journey forwards, we cannot go 'back' to normal – whatever that is.*

Having some awareness of the map of grief also enables would-be helpers to see how inappropriate it is to push a person on too fast. What is happening with the church friends is that they want her to be at stage four (for their own reasons) when she is only at stage two.

One of the factors seems to be that for the onlooker time feels

## Suggested Dos and Don'ts

### Do

- attempt to enter into solidarity with her pain and grief, being ready to listen and understand
- let her weep without attempting to stop the tears in order to leave you feeling more comfortable
- encourage her to be patient with herself and not to put on a show just to please the church
- be aware that she will be emotionally vulnerable at this time
- help her with her any practical needs
- talk about her husband with affection
- reassure her that she is not going mad
- reassure her that her care of him was beyond reproach
- look after yourself and perhaps have a friend outside the situation to support you
- in your caring, bring the unspoken confidence that Good Friday will lead on to Easter Day.

### Don't

- belittle what has happened in any way
- pass judgment on her feelings
- say you understand her feelings if you don't
- keep your distance because you feel inexperienced in grief
- share *your* problems with her; she has enough to handle
- say that it could have been worse in some way
- say that everything will work out all right in the end
- prevent her from seeing a psychiatrist, should her doctor recommend this
- try to pray the grief away or put your feelings of what she should be doing into prayer with her

longer than for the grief-stricken person, for whom time stands still and the pain of their loss may feel as real as yesterday.

Another issue is that we have discarded the social conventions once associated with mourning which allowed bereaved people space, time, and aloneness to do their grieving.

The depression of grief needs, for example, to be viewed positively, as a kind of protective cloak which we need.

Church people require this level of sensitivity towards those in grief, rather than expecting them to feel better as a result of the church praying for them. The pain of loss is not something to be prayed away: it is a healing journey to go through.

As Brother Roger of Taizé puts it: 'When we love we open a door to pain which can never be healed.'

At the peak of grief, doctors are often tempted to prescribe anti-depressant medication as a caring response. This enables the doctor to feel active in reducing distress and may indeed help restore a sleep pattern if this is a continuing problem.

On the less helpful side, medication during natural grieving can suppress the process, leaving the mourning incomplete. But it is hard not to do something to ease the pain. Your friend is probably so thankful that you are able to stay alongside her.

Henri Nouwen writes:

Let us not underestimate how hard it is to be compassionate. Compassion is hard because it requires the inner disposition to go with others to the place where they are weak, vulnerable, lonely and broken.

But this is not our spontaneous response to suffering. What we desire most is to do away with suffering by fleeing from it or finding a quick cure for it. As busy, active, relevant ministers (friends, doctors), we want to earn our bread by making a real contribution.

This means first and foremost doing something to show that our presence makes a difference. And so we ignore our greatest gift, which is our ability to enter into solidarity with those who suffer.

The implication of what the friends at church are saying is that something has gone wrong. It *is* possible for grief to become suppressed or to be unusually prolonged. But given the timescale you describe we consider your friend's reactions to be quite normal.

What also often happens in the peak of grief is that relationships become strained and difficult.

Has it occurred to you that in trying to come to terms with her widowhood the old associations with church friends may be extremely painful − especially if their own partners are still alive?

## Sensitive support

In terms of advice, then, we would not suggest any heavy intervention. Freud gave us the notion of 'grief work' and recommended that grieving people were best left alone to do it. But sensitive support is required to enable the process.

Your friend needs permission to go on grieving. She may well need to keep talking about her husband and especially the time of his illness. You may have to indicate that you are happy to listen to the same old stories. The needle is not stuck in the groove, rather she needs to repeat herself until the acuteness of the pain is out of her system.

Ministers often keep a record of the anniversaries of funerals they conduct and it may be good for her to meet up with the minister who took her husband's funeral. Meeting a year on and maybe sharing a little service of some kind, or just chatting, helps to process the memories of the death and the funeral.

Your friend may find it a help to talk to someone a little more detached than her circle of friends, such as a bereavement counsellor.

Counselling is particularly helpful when there is no network of friends and church around to be supportive, when another crisis follows hard on the heels of a bereavement or when the circumstances surrounding death are particularly traumatic. If a partnership is already in deep water when a terminal illness is diagnosed then skilled help is invaluable.

In this country, the only national organization to provide bereavement counselling on a wide scale is CRUSE, the address of which is at the end of this article. Hospices often have their own bereavement services to support the families they have been involved with.

## Further reactions

Even in the years ahead you may be wondering if you would realize when your friend needs counselling help, possibly in conjunction with medication. There are a number of indications that this may be so:

— she may be unable to speak about her loss without fresh intense sadness, maybe even years after her bereavement;

— there is a continuous overreaction to other losses, for example, to a friend's miscarriage;

— there continues to be a series of losses in her life;

— she seems unwilling to move material possessions belonging to her husband, sometimes even years after the event;

— physical symptoms similar to those of the deceased recur, often annually around the anniversary of the death;

— she makes radical life-style changes after bereavement and even excludes friends and relatives of her husband;

— she persists with guilt and lowered self-esteem which cause the grieving process to become stuck;

— she persistently avoids reality, e.g. signing cards as from both herself and her husband and even booking two tickets for a holiday.

If you see some of these reactions in your friend, she will still need you to befriend her but encourage her to seek further help.

We have not said much about how our faith relates directly to the process of grief. It is of course highly relevant. The pain and struggle of our loving and losing is perhaps only made bearable through the power of the Spirit of Christ.

We pray that you might develop an unspoken confidence in his strength to take you and your friend through Good Friday to Easter Day.

> Here might I stay and sing:
> no story so divine;
> never was love, dear King,
> *never was grief like thine!*

This is my friend,
in whose sweet praise
I all my days
could gladly spend.

*Samuel Crossman*

## Helpful reading

*Living Through Grief* by H Baumann (Lion)

*All in the End is Harvest* ed A Whitaker (Darton, Longman & Todd/Cruse)

*A Grief Observed* by C S Lewis (Faber & Faber)

*Letting Go* by Ian Ainsworth-Smith and Peter Speck (SPCK)

*Requiem Healing* by Michael Mitton and Russ Parker (Darton, Longman & Todd)

## Address

CRUSE – Bereavement Care, 126 Sheen Road, Richmond, Surrey TW9 1UR Tel: 0181 940 4818.

# *14* Facing AIDS: How Can Others Understand?

**Q** I am gay. Three years ago I began to feel unwell with tiredness, diarrhoea and weight loss. My doctor referred me to a hospital where I was found to be HIV positive.

I have still not developed AIDS, yet I am writing because I feel angry and helpless. Your article on anger gave me the courage to write.

I feel isolated, unloved and the recipient of patronizing pity both from the church and the medical profession.

How can I move on to find quality of life – for however long? How can those around me be helped to understand what I am going through?

**A** Thank you for your question. It is one we have struggled to answer and yet we felt we could not leave it in the pending tray.

We feel the enormity of your pain and also are aware of the pain within the church and society. Everyone's struggle with their own reactions puts you at the sharp end, not only of your own feelings but also of theirs.

By now, we expect you are better informed than some of the doctors you meet with regard to most aspects of HIV and AIDS. Nevertheless, for the sake of our readers, we think it would be helpful to sketch out the four usual stages of illness that, barring the unexpected, precede the development of full-blown AIDS.

The more information people around you have, the less fantasizing and hysteria will prevail.

# THE PROGRESSION OF HIV

**Category 1** This is the initial stage of actual infection. You feel as though you have flu and present to the doctor an illness not unlike glandular fever.

The usual features may include a temperature, swollen glands, sweats, aching muscles, sore throat, headache, upset stomach and even a rash.

A blood test taken at that time for HIV may be negative. But it offers no real assurance, because it may take six weeks or more before becoming positive.

Despite a possible negative test, the virus is in the blood and can be transmitted to others.

**Category 2** At this stage you may begin to block off reality because you feel well again. The occasional bout of thrush in the mouth might remind you that all is not as it should be.

**Category 3** You continue to feel well but may now notice that the lymph glands around your body have become swollen. These glands are felt as rounded firm lumps on both sides of the neck, in the armpits, at the elbows and in the groin.

**Category 4** It seems that about half of those at this stage of HIV infection will develop full-blown AIDS within ten years. But it is very much hoped that new treatments being developed will prevent or at least delay this progression.

At this point, the virus becomes more active again and makes itself felt in a number of debilitating ways. Sweats, lethargy, headache and symptoms of thrush return along with a dry cough, muscle weakness, diarrhoea and possibly brownish purple bumps on the skin.

# LIVING WITH LOSS

We would encourage you to reflect on some of the losses you are facing. We have written before about the feelings of loss that those with a possibly fatal illness may experience. For you, there are extra burdens to bear and it would be good if your friends could realize a little of what you are having to cope with. It is hardly surprising that you feel angry.

### Loss of relationships

You may already be facing the loss of family and friends, especially if they had not realized that you are gay.

Your feelings of isolation may be fuelled by the thought that people will possibly tend to keep their distance, fearing illogically and wrongly that social contact carries the risk of catching the virus from you.

Many will find it difficult to relate and so avoid you. They may end up being patronizing or being overconcerned, as if you were an invalid.

You will need to give thought to what it is right to tell them; bear in mind that information tends to get distorted and exaggerated as it travels round the community or even the church congregation!

### Loss of identity

You may be facing loss of your employment, loss of status in society and even loss of your role in church. The position of respect within your family may be lessened.

Hopefully, you are already finding a new identity and role as you strive to build bridges, inform and, above all, break down barriers of fear.

### Loss of control

Yes, the virus has to some extent taken control of your life. The endless time-consuming hospital visits will help to keep you as fit as possible. The effect of different treatments needs to be monitored and so regular check-ups really are important.

Maybe some of your friends with AIDS will have suffered episodes of brain impairment. This can happen early or late in AIDS; it is scary and it best to know who can look after you should this happen. It isn't common, but it is better to be prepared. Perhaps see if there is a home care team covering your area.

### Loss of sexual expression

The relationship with your partner has had to change to prevent transmission of the virus. Physical fulfilment may be lacking and this can highlight areas of loss between you.

At a time when your cry for love is at its loudest, you are left aching for a depth of togetherness that cannot be. That again leaves you feeling isolated.

### Loss of body image

Marked weight loss can bring a further knock to your lowered self-esteem, as can those skin blemishes that may develop. It may help to choose clothes that disguise your low weight and leave you feeling good. You can buy camouflage make-up to cover up skin changes that are visible to others.

### Loss of children

Although you are gay, harbouring a secret longing for a child is not unusual. Now this opportunity is denied to you, as there is a high chance that your child would be infected too.

### Loss of life style

If you are unable to work, it may be hard to make your finances stretch to meet your needs. The few luxuries that have eased your pain may have to go. Obtaining a mortgage or life insurance policy could be difficult now too.

There are so many losses to face, each one triggering further pain. You will find some losses come late, some come and leave almost unnoticed, while others make a terrible deep wound. It is not surprising that you feel helpless.

## PSYCHOLOGICAL HURDLES

We will highlight some of the hurdles of your journey so that some around you will see the need to stay close to you and to share as best they can.

Handling the original diagnosis must have been fairly overwhelming once the anaesthetic of disbelief had worn off. New treatments hint at the progression of disease and yet the abandoning of medication because of intolerable side-effects or ineffectiveness can leave you in despair.

If full-blown AIDS does develop, the challenges presented need sharing – your feelings will need to be heard and understood.

If you keep too much to yourself, you may experience panics that cause sweats, shaking and diarrhoea, just like your illness.

Depression and suicidal thoughts are common. We would encourage you to share these, not only with someone you can trust in the church, but also with your doctor.

Thought processes and behaviour patterns can be all over the place at this time. Suspicions and worries that have no foundation can fill your mind and we would urge you not to handle them alone.

You may find all this rather scary and depressing. But, hopefully, you have realized from seeing others who are HIV positive that, even if you have AIDS eventually, you can feel well most of the time with good symptomatic treatment and proper support.

## FRIENDS AND HELPERS

Your anger is probably pushing your friends and carers away from you. If you manage to focus on your grievances rather than on individuals, it might create an opportunity for friends to come closer and to respond with the tangible love and compassion that should be yours. Meaningful hugs can lift isolation in no time.

It may be that people have distanced themselves from you because the thought of AIDS has disturbed their sense of personal security. Your illness is a reminder that we cannot always control our environment and this is an uncomfortable reminder of our mortality.

Fear generated in this way can even lead on to hate, prejudice and rejection just when you are asking for love, solidarity and acceptance.

Basically, your would-be helpers and friends at church need to do their own work on coming to terms both with their mortality and with HIV/AIDS-related illnesses.

Until and unless they have begun to do this, you will not find them to be highly constructive in the way they are able to cope with you. (This again sadly is true for many who are sick in our churches.)

There are a number of churches, usually in major towns and cities, which are deeply involved with HIV/AIDS situations and are highly sensitive to them. There are also some Christian projects (see resources list below), again mainly in London and the cities, that will help.

If you are not in reach of these, you need to seek out specialist help to get the understanding required to help you with the intensity of your feelings and reactions. Most health authorities have a team devoted to working alongside people with HIV/AIDS, including counsellors trained in awareness of the kind of issues raised. Your doctor should be able to direct you here, and the church needs to know that such resources exist.

Self-help groups can be very supportive and you may discover a new role from joining one of these. Your church home group, if you have one, while being vital for prayer and practical support, is no substitute for a self-help group.

We mention practical support, realizing that at some stage this will need to be skilled and informed. Organizations like ACET have home care teams covering London, parts of the south coast, the East Midlands, Edinburgh, Dundee and Glasgow. They give their carefully selected volunteers several weeks' training and even provide a twenty-four-hour on-call service.

In you, O Lord, I take my refuge
Let me never be put to shame.
In your justice, set me free.
Into your hands I commend my
    spirit.
It is you who will redeem me,
    Lord.

In the face of all my foes
I am a reproach,
An object of scorn to my
    neighbours
And of fear to my friends.

Those who see me in the street
Run far away from me.
I am like a dead man, forgotten in
    men's hearts,
Like a thing thrown away.

But as for me, I trust in you, Lord,
I say: 'You are my God.'
My life is in your hands, deliver
    me
From the hands of those who hate
    me.

Let your face shine on your
    servant.
Safe in your love.
Be strong, let your heart take
    courage,
All who hope in the Lord.

Paraphrase by Jeanette Renouf
(From Psalm 22)

## REACTING TO LIFESTYLE

We hope that you can have patience with the people at church. Almost certainly, many of them are struggling to relate well to you and you could be a real means of extending their education and pastoral sensitivity.

It is important for your own protection that you only risk opening yourself up with those who are affirming and non-judgmental.

Don't feel you are being unspiritual if you decline invitations to 'repent'! Broadly speaking, even if a church has worked through its position on explicit homosexuality, you will be an uncomfortable person for many to have around. But we hope and pray you will stick in there.

We hope that as well as getting specialist advice and counselling, you will find some relationships of trust and sensitivity in the church.

One of the difficulties has been that, partly because of rejection by the rest of society, gays have grouped and socialized together. You will be doing everyone a favour if you develop relationships with friends of both sexes.

Christians can so easily reject those with a different lifestyle, yet we have little doubt that if Jesus was on earth today he would make a beeline for you. He certainly made a point of embracing those rejected by society in his own day, e.g. by reaching out to touch those with leprosy.

Throughout the ages Christians have believed that homosexual practices are sinful. Yet they have also recognized that Jesus is the only one who has the right to judge. We acknowledge with sorrow the truth that all of us have sinned and fallen short of God's glory – whatever our sexual orientation. And we are all called to reflect the boundless generosity of God's grace.

## JESUS AS YOUR FRIEND

We really hope and pray that on your journey in life you will increasingly come to know Jesus as your friend. There is no question that you are his friend and that he knows the awful experience of being viewed as 'of the devil'. So be encouraged in your walk with him.

Receiving the sacraments, especially holy communion and possibly anointing with oil, can assure you of God's presence and offer you his strength and healing. You may well feel that prayer and/or anointing is best done quietly and unobtrusively, and we hope your minister can make this possible for you.

Part of the abundance of life which Jesus brings is that gift of the quality of living which you are seeking. As one person, herself disabled, put it, there is all the difference in the world between 'suffering from' and 'living with' an illness. We hope that you will develop the capacity to live life in the fullness of the present moment, whatever the future brings.

David learnt a great deal from a young man living with AIDS who, even when very ill, took up learning the piano and enjoyed this as something he had hitherto not been able to do.

People with AIDS often have a remarkable creativity in poetry, art and music. The poignancy of a life-threatening condition, once it is harnessed, seems to heighten the quality and creativity of living.

Perhaps George Herbert sums up all this rather better than we can in his poem 'Bitter Sweet'.

Ah my dear angry Lord,
Since thou dost live, yet strike;
Cast down, yet help afford;
Sure I will do the like.

I will complain, yet praise;
I will bewail, approve;
And all my sour-sweet days
I will lament, and love.

## Helpful reading

*Sexual Integrity — the answer to AIDS* by Jack Dominian (Darton, Longman & Todd)
*Evangelical Christians and Gay Rights* by Michael Vasey (Grove)
*Living on the Edge* by Michael Kelly (Marshall Pickering)
*A Place of Growth* by Marcetti and Lunn (Darton, Longman & Todd)
*The Truth about AIDS* by Patrick Dixon (Kingsway)

## Resources

ACET (AIDS Care Education and Training), PO Box 1323, London W54 5TF
The Terrence Higgins Trust, 52-54 Gray's Inn Road, London WC1X 8CX
Body Positive, St Cuthbert's Centre, Earl's Court, London SW5 9EB
London Lighthouse, 178 Lancaster Road, London W11 1QY
Mildmay Mission Hospital, Hackney Road, London E2 7NA

# *15* Where Is the Healing in Suffering?

**Q** I've read some of your articles and found them interesting. My forty-year-old wife is very disabled with multiple sclerosis and I struggle to make sense of what 'healing' means when I am so surrounded by suffering that goes on and gets worse. What can you say about this?

**A** Your question cannot be answered glibly and we are only too aware of the enormous hurdles you and your wife are facing. We suspect yours is the heart cry of so many who seek to find healing but have to remain with suffering.

## SETTING THE SCENE

There are at least 60,000 people with multiple sclerosis in the United Kingdom. Unfortunately, your wife is amongst the two-thirds of those afflicted who become significantly disabled by the disease. Nonetheless, the reality of MS is that it does not usually shorten life. The disease is characterized by exacerbations and remissions and until more is understood doctors have to concentrate on damping down acute flare-ups, attempting to prevent relapses and above all, bringing relief to symptoms. Progress in research has been slow, probably because of the complex nature of MS. At present most attempts to influence the cause of the disease are based on the assumption that, irrespective of initial causes – be they genetic, environmental or both – the nervous system is damaged because of an upset in the workings of the immune system. It is also possible that a persistent viral infection prevents the immune system from recovering suffi-

111

ciently to overcome the disease. Drugs aimed at boosting immunity have shown encouraging results in significantly delaying the onset of disability but, as yet, medicine does not offer a cure.

With the ups and downs of disease activity, your hopes will inevitably be raised as physical improvement occurs in response to prayer. These hopes may later be dashed should symptoms recur. Part of your present struggle to make sense of it all is indicative of the enormous cost to you both of these emotional swings. Recognition of further losses brings frustration, anger and even a sense of alien-ation from God. Until you can let go of needing to understand what God is up to, that his ways are not our ways, it is not easy to reach a place of acceptance that he is in control whatever. If together you can reach this place, you will find there is more energy for everyday living and loving as you give less attention to the purposes behind the hassles of the present moment. Coping with a seemingly endless disease is not helped by focusing on new medical regimes and a daily assess-ment of the severity of each symptom. Love and prayer from those around you can transform even the darkest valley and bring a sense of hope, purpose and meaning. Denial and resistance lead on to accep-tance and integration as God touches you in body, mind and spirit, whether physical healing follows or not.

You have together to face the possibility of physical cure eluding you this side of heaven. We sense you have done this and are strug-gling with the seeming pointlessness of this illness. There is no slick answer as we face up to the mysteries of suffering in our world. Your anguish is complex because it is not simply about your wife's outlook in clinical terms. It is about a daily struggle which involves her facing what is happening to her; you watching her facing that; you caring in a thousand practical ways which are demanding and time-consuming. This may well mean you have to rearrange your own work or even abandon it. Caring can become a full-time job. Added to this are your own reactions to your wife's incapacity, the grief and the stress of which place enormous pressures on the marriage relationship. Perhaps nothing tests those marriage vows quite as much as long-term disabling illness.

What does enable us to keep going against all the odds if there is not some sense of real meaning and purpose? It was Frankl who wrote, 'If there is a meaning in life at all, then there must be a meaning in suffering. Suffering is an ineradicable part of life . . . without suffering and human death life cannot be complete.' We recognize that for you and your wife it is vitally important to discover some meaning in the awfulness of your struggles. So hopefully you will forgive us if we expound a little on what Christians can make of suffering and also what we think healing really means in the light of it. We can only hope it may fit at some points within your own experience.

## HEALING CURE AS NORMAL

It sounds as if like most of us you have been influenced by recent healing theology, whereby since the seventies the charismatic renewal movement has tended implicitly or explicitly towards the view that Christ, in healing us, does away with our suffering. Clearly, if held to blindly, this view will not help you because it suggests that to go on suffering is somehow wrong and not likely to be God's will for you.

In itself it was largely a reaction to the previously strong teaching about suffering as 'redemptive': this could over-exalt it by saying, for example, that we were closer to the wounds of Christ if we suffered and that we should passively accept it and bear 'our cross'. A martyr complex does not help anyone! Nevertheless, our feeling would be that now we need to reverse the trend so that suffering and healing do not have to be seen as opposed. At Burrswood, the founder Dorothy Kerin was herself the recipient of a miraculous cure by the Lord. She predated current healing theory and prayed, 'By the bruising of my whole life, strengthen me with sympathy for every wounded soul . . .' She found God's meaning in and prayerfully drew his strength from her wounds and bruises. Burrswood was founded on a sign, a wonder, an outpouring of the love of God that restored one life, that of

Dorothy Kerin, and through her, transformed so many more. Yet so often we encounter suffering that has no horizon. We endeavour to believe that the losses which are evident in those who are suffering provide potential for gain.

## A PLACE FOR REDEMPTIVE SUFFERING

In the light of the reality that all of us face some measure of suffering on a daily basis, and that all of us are mortal, it may well be that the redeeming of suffering is in fact more normative than the relieving of it. In our work together we would sometimes want to refer to this as a kind of 'healing within suffering' – there is a wholeness which is at an altogether deeper level of experience than simply being made better. As we have mentioned before, it is the difference between 'living with' rather than 'suffering from' an illness or condition. When we pray for healing we are praying for this miracle to happen, perhaps more than the miracle of release from all suffering. The latter may not be achieved until the light of heaven itself dawns. We are talking about finding the abundance of the Spirit within our limitations, truly the power of the Spirit to go through what we face in the strength of Christ who has endured the cross. Therefore could it be that the Christ who demonstrated the power of the Spirit within his own physical deterioration on the cross gives you the grace of his Spirit to live within your increasing losses and limitations?

It may then be possible for you to draw both understanding and strength from the insight that Christ went through suffering and not round it. What he went through is, of course, not for us to go through, for we are not called upon to save the world. But that is not to say that, as some simplistic theories have suggested, he removes all burdens from us. Rather, he has pioneered a new way for us to follow, running the race of faith 'looking unto him' (Hebrews 12:1).

## PRAYING WITH FAITH?

Some would say we are *not* praying 'with faith', meaning that our expectation level is too low. But we would argue that our faith is faith in the living Lord himself, not in what we hope he might do for us. We therefore pray in the power of the Spirit of the Lord (himself 'made perfect through suffering' Hebrews 2:10) that he could complete and perfect this growth in us whether he relieves the suffering or not. To be the more fully healed and made whole for a Christian means to be given the strength of the Christ who suffered to bear our bad experiences as well as our good ones: and to 'believe' in the midst of the bad as well as the good.

## GROWTH POINTS?

Jesus himself was 'made perfect through suffering'. Certainly, if we can bear it, there is nothing quite like adversity for enabling us to grow. This can never satisfy us as the whole meaning of suffering. Nevertheless, we may be helped to bear it if we can see it achieving something. You may already have noticed that your suffering can bring growth. Perhaps there are things that have happened for you that would not have happened without the illness. Good things may even have happened between the two of you or within your family which will show you God at work in it.

## MEANINGLESS

When the sense of growth through your suffering deserts you, and it surely will at times, you may be faced with the sheer meaninglessness of it. You are left with the anguished scream of feeling hopeless and abandoned. But Christ is also there by his own abandonment and cry of dereliction on the cross. We think of someone we will call Doreen. Her husband had died at Burrswood some time before and she returned to us with secondary cancer for terminal care. She was hurting, not only because her liver was larger by the day, but also because her son had seemingly distanced himself from her. (Unknown to her, his business had collapsed and in trying to keep this from his mother, he had become seemingly remote to her.) Doreen had prayed and prayed in her weakness and distress and felt God had not listened. 'Tell God how you feel,' Gareth suggested. 'God, why have you abandoned me?' she cried. After a while he commented 'Now you are with Jesus on the cross.' Her blue eyes lit up with joy. 'I'll stay with him; that helps so much.' Doreen's last few days were filled with a new sense of purpose and peace. Because Christ also cried out, 'Why have you forsaken me?' to the Father so our own place of felt godlessness is in fact a place where he is paradoxically present.

This gives us the possibility, as George Bennett said, of 'breaking our heart into the agelong heartbreak of Christ'. Whatever the philosophical answer to the age-old question 'Does God still suffer?' we would want to affirm the lines of the hymn:

And when human hearts are aching
Under sorrow's iron rod
Then they find the self-same aching
Deep within the heart of God.

## OUR SUFFERING IN HIS

There is some sense of the ongoing suffering of Christ being completed in us in Colossians 1:24. Dorothy Kerin picked up this verse when she talked of the way in which we can 'glorify God in our sicknesses and offer (our) suffering in unison with his . . . towards the filling up of the cup.' Could this mean for you that you find a way to put your sorrow and suffering into his? Feeling it is somehow mysteriously part of the timeless offering of Christ's suffering? Technically this is perhaps something of what 'redemptive suffering' means.

On a practical level we do not know your usual prayer patterns but, to enable something of what we have been describing here to happen, it may help you to have a crucifix in your sights. Receiving holy communion can also be a God-given way of taking in, in the here-and-now, what the Prayer Book called 'all other benefits of his passion'.

## DEFINITIONS

Any definition of healing for us then has to be far wider than simply receiving a cure. We are grateful for the Mission Statement of Burrswood 'aiming to work within the mystery of healing and suffering'. In the area of healing the Christian faith is not problem-solving but mystery-encountering. To be healed or made whole in the Gospels seems to speak of God's love and power, and is a sign of his kingdom breaking through into our suffering world. Healing is perhaps a process by which we are restored to a state of right-related-ness to and dependence on God. It is in this sense that all can be healed though not all are cured.

A memorable example of this was when we met at Burrswood someone we'll call Katherine. She had come for two weeks' 'holiday' with her husband so that he and other helpers could have a break from some of the practical caring. Katherine had motor neurone disease and her one remaining movement was blinking. The staff around her had to carry a sheet with Morse code in their pockets because this was her only means of communication – long and short blinks! We thought that her care would present a great challenge to the team, that she would have tremendous fears and emotional needs and yet we encountered someone who was totally at peace. Her eyes radiated the love and presence of Christ and we were all enlarged through knowing

---

### *When illness has no horizon:*

- Try to stay with reality and look for measures to transform that rather than living in a dream because reality is hell;
- Be ready to receive, not only from those around you, but also from each other;
- Avoid isolation. You both need a 'travelling companion' who will share your pain and confusion rather than being over-ready to provide 'good advice';
- Be aware of the triggers to your anger and grief which may come and go. Rather than distribute this pain around your friends, try to tell God about it;
- Acknowledge your own doubts and uncertainties rather than defending God or overspiritualizing your hell;
- Hold on to the glimpses of joy amidst the pain; the tiny but important reminders of God's love – the seeds of resurrection.

---

her. We received so much from her and realized that on encountering Katherine, healing had to be redefined. We had not met anyone so at peace with herself, her illness and, above all, with God.


## CONCLUSION

The glory and the agony of what we are struggling to say cannot be learned on paper or out of books, but only in the wear and tear, in the blood, sweat and tears of what you are experiencing. God be with you!


### *Helpful reading*
*Celebration* by Margaret Spufford (Fount)
*Mud and Stars* by Robert Twycross et al (Sobell)
*Face to Face* by Frances Young (T & T Clark)
*Healing and Suffering* by Paul Fielden (Darton, Longman & Todd)

## BURRSWOOD

Burrswood is a Christian Centre for Medical and Spiritual Care. People find the healing of Jesus Christ through skilled nursing, medical expertise, counselling and prayer. Stillness and beauty provide space for the Holy Spirit's transforming work in every area of life. Many who come for a short stay are enabled to do so irrespective of their means.

The community of Burrswood, with its individual gifts and abilities, is committed to bringing together medicine and Christianity and to working within the mystery of healing and suffering. It aims to keep the love of God at the heart of care and to be a sign of the Kingdom of God in a hurting world.

For more information about the work of Burrswood and admissions to the Medical Centre and Guest House do please contact:-

> The Admissions Office
> Burrswood
> Groombridge
> Tunbridge Wells
> Kent TN3 9PY
>
> Tel: 01892 863818 or 863637.